WATERLOO
Middle School Library

796.357
MIL

ON THE BOARDS

Author

Van Milverstedt

Photography

Heinz Kluetmeier
Vernon Biever

©Advanced Learning Concepts, Inc., 1975

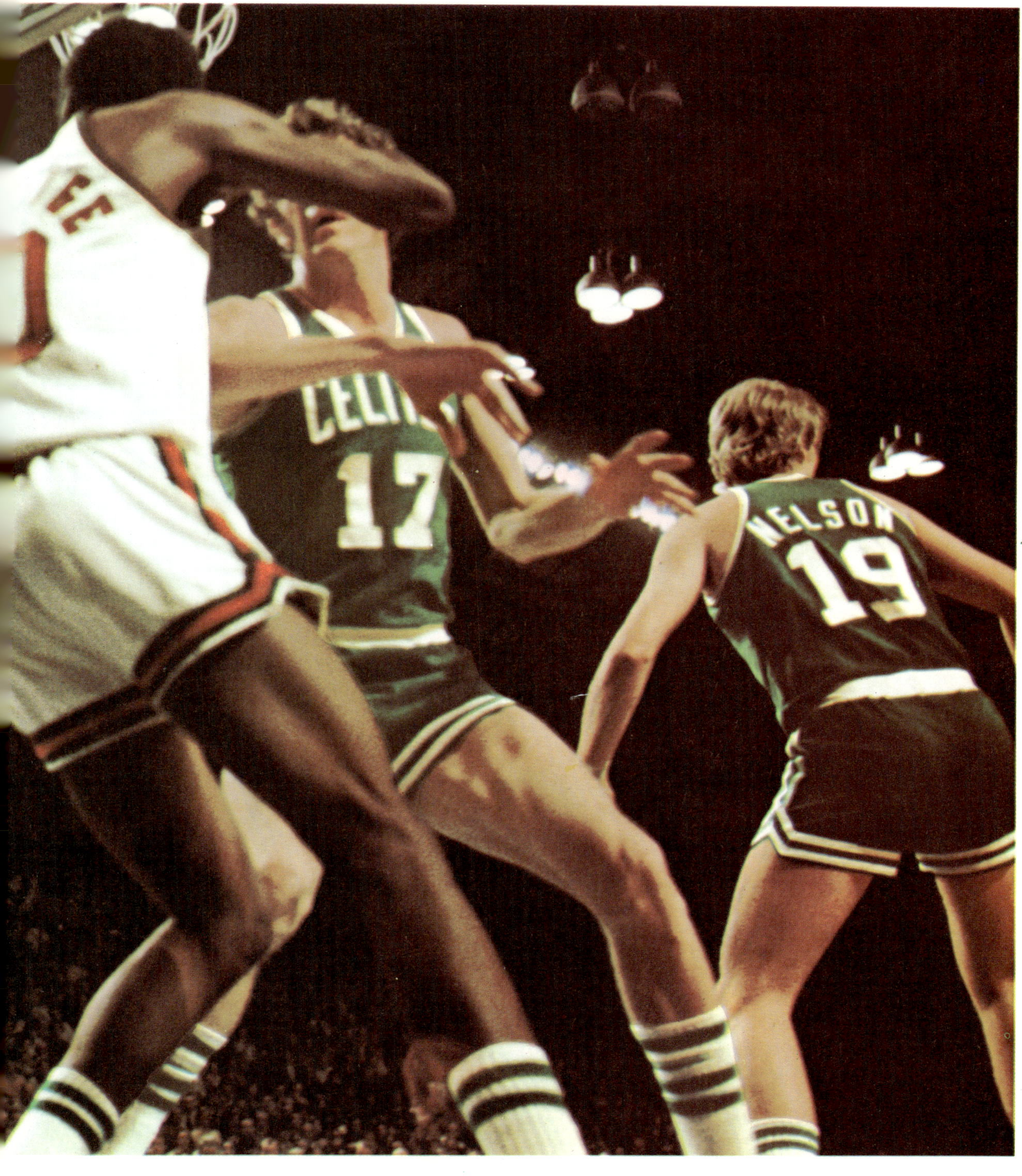
17
NELSON
19

Copyright © 1975 by Advanced Learning Concepts, Inc.

International copyrights reserved in all countries.

No part of this book may be reproduced in any form whatsoever without the written permission of the publisher.

Library of Congress Number: 75-1128

ISBN 0-8172-0209-9

Published by **Advanced Learning Concepts, Inc.**
Milwaukee, Wisconsin

A Product of **Advanced Learning Concepts, Inc.
and Follett Publishing Company**
A Division of Follett Corporation
Chicago, Illinois

Contents

1 It Beats Working   6

2 Thwunk! The Dunk!   12

3 More Than Just Fun   20

4 Talent And Hard Work   28

5 In A Jam   34

6 A Whole Different Thing   42

7 Rally   54

   Pre-Reading Aids   65

   Discussion Questions   72

   Related Activities   73

1
It Beats Working

Artemus Jones is six feet five in his calfskin boots. When he walks into the crowded restaurant across the street from the Arena two hours before the NBA championship game, some of the people turn and stare. To some of them, anybody that big has got to be a basketball player. They check him out close.

Arty sits down and orders a cup of coffee. A guy at the next table is watching him out of the corner of his eye.

"Hey," says the guy, "aren't you Bobby Dandridge?"

Arty laughs.

"Are you kiddin', man? Me and that cat don't look anything alike. We're both tall and skinny, that's all."

The fan is not quite sure.

"Yeah? Well you sure look like him. Do you play ball?"

"Naw, not any more," says Arty. "Just mess around mostly, tossin' 'em up. Mostly, I just write about it."

"Yeah? What do you write?" asks the fan. "You with the papers? Which one?"

"The *News*," says Arty. "I do a column."

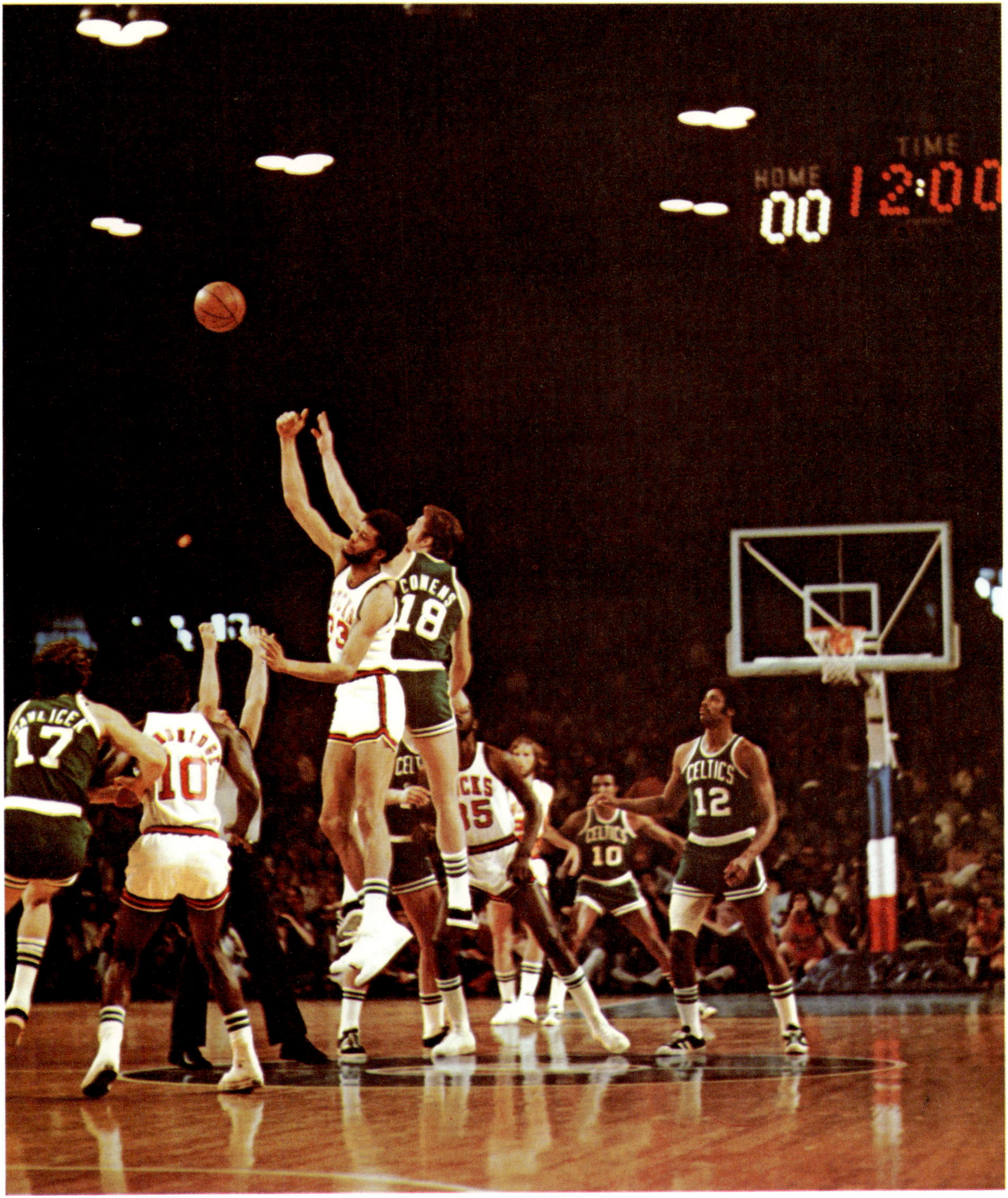
TIME
HOME
00
12:00
COWENS
18
17
10
CELTICS
12
CELTICS
10

The fan's face lights up.

"Yeah, sure, I know you — you're that guy Jones. Hey, I read your stuff." He turns to his friends. "This is that newspaper guy, Arty Jones. He covers the Bucks and writes a column for the *News*."

"Hey, Arty, who's gonna win the game?"

Before Arty can answer, a small curly-haired man in an Army field jacket steps up to Arty's table. He lays his hand on Arty's shoulder. He is loaded down with three camera bags slung over his shoulders. His pockets bulge with film. He is Monte McCoy, the *News* sports photographer.

"Telephone for Mr. Jones. Telephone for Artemus Jones," calls out Monte in a loud voice. "Right this way, please." He takes Arty by the elbow and leads him swiftly away. Arty is laughing as they melt into the crowd.

"I've got a table over in the corner," says Monte. "There isn't a fan within yards."

As they leave, the fan is hollering over the noise of the crowd.

"I may read ya', Jones, but I don't always agree with ya'!"

"That's fair enough," says Monte. "If half of them even understand you, what more can you ask?"

They sit down. "Saved you again," he says, grinning. "It must be tough to be famous."

Arty shakes his head. "Now if I was only making the money to go along with the fame."

"How can you complain?" asks Monte. "How can anyone complain who makes as much as you for going to basketball games? What a deal. You should have to work for a living."

"That's what they all say," says Arty. "But what about the deadlines? What about the

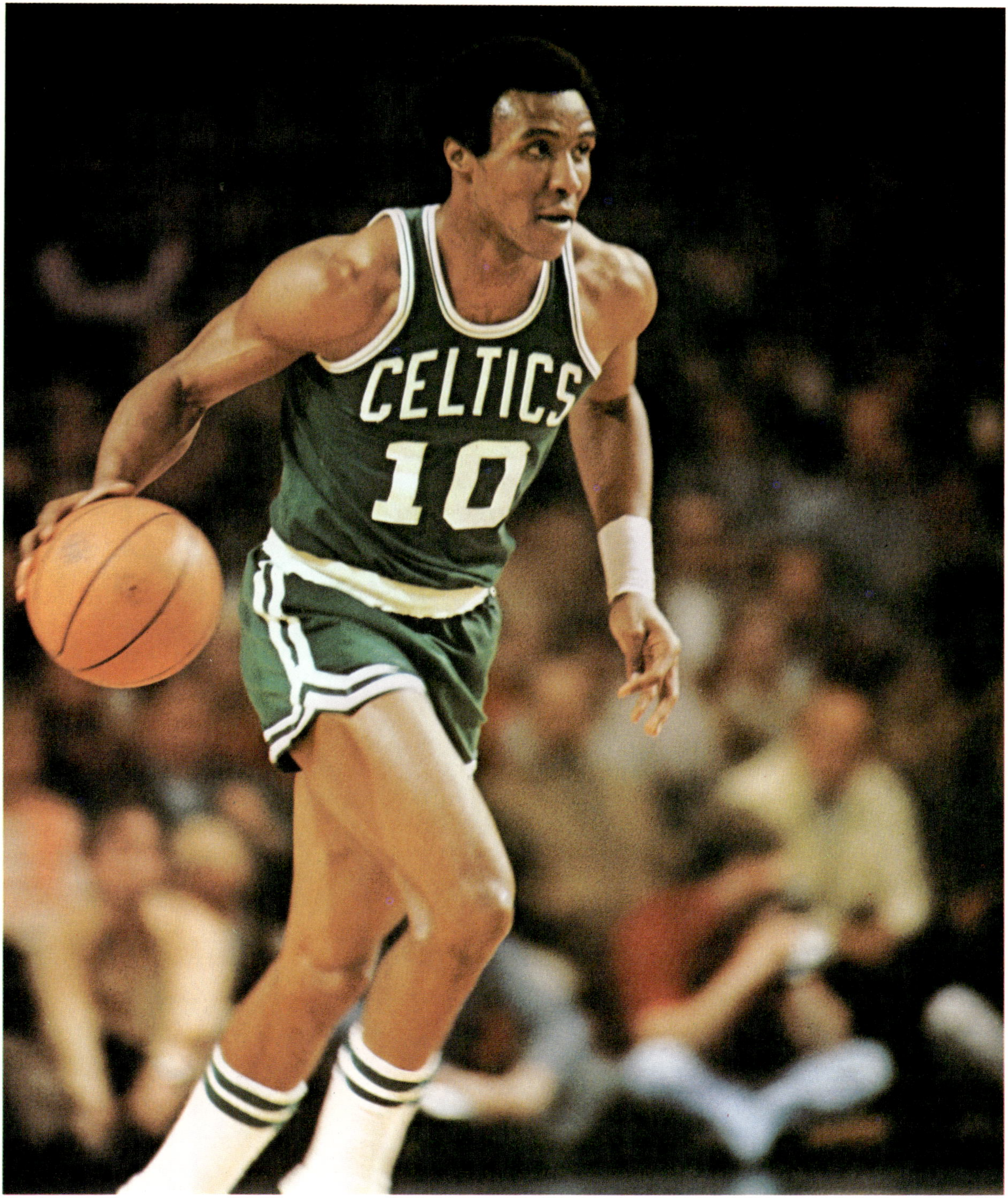
CELTICS
10

travel and the crazy hours? What about the times when your head is blocked and you're sitting there at the typewriter with an editor back in the office screaming for your story? Man, that's no bargain. And how about these fans? How about having to talk to jerk fans and jerk players all the time?"

"C'mon," says Monte, "you love it, you love it. And besides, it beats working."

Arty nods and sips his coffee. "Yeah, I suppose part of that is right. I know my old man still doesn't understand. He keeps askin' me when I'm gonna get a serious job. He thinks I should have been a teacher."

Arty thinks about that a bit. He sits there nursing his coffee on a cold and rainy night, waiting to get paid for watching the Boston Celtics play the Milwaukee Bucks for the NBA championship. He thinks about where he came from and how he got to be where he is. He thinks about his old man back in Miami, working hard as a porter in a hotel. Miami is a long way back there, years and miles away.

Monte McCoy picks up on the mood. "Where's your head?" he asks.

"It's a long story."

"I suppose," says Monte. "I never knew a sportswriter who could tell a short one. Want to spread it around? We've got some time."

"Sure," says Arty.

The little photographer sits back and waits for Arty to begin.

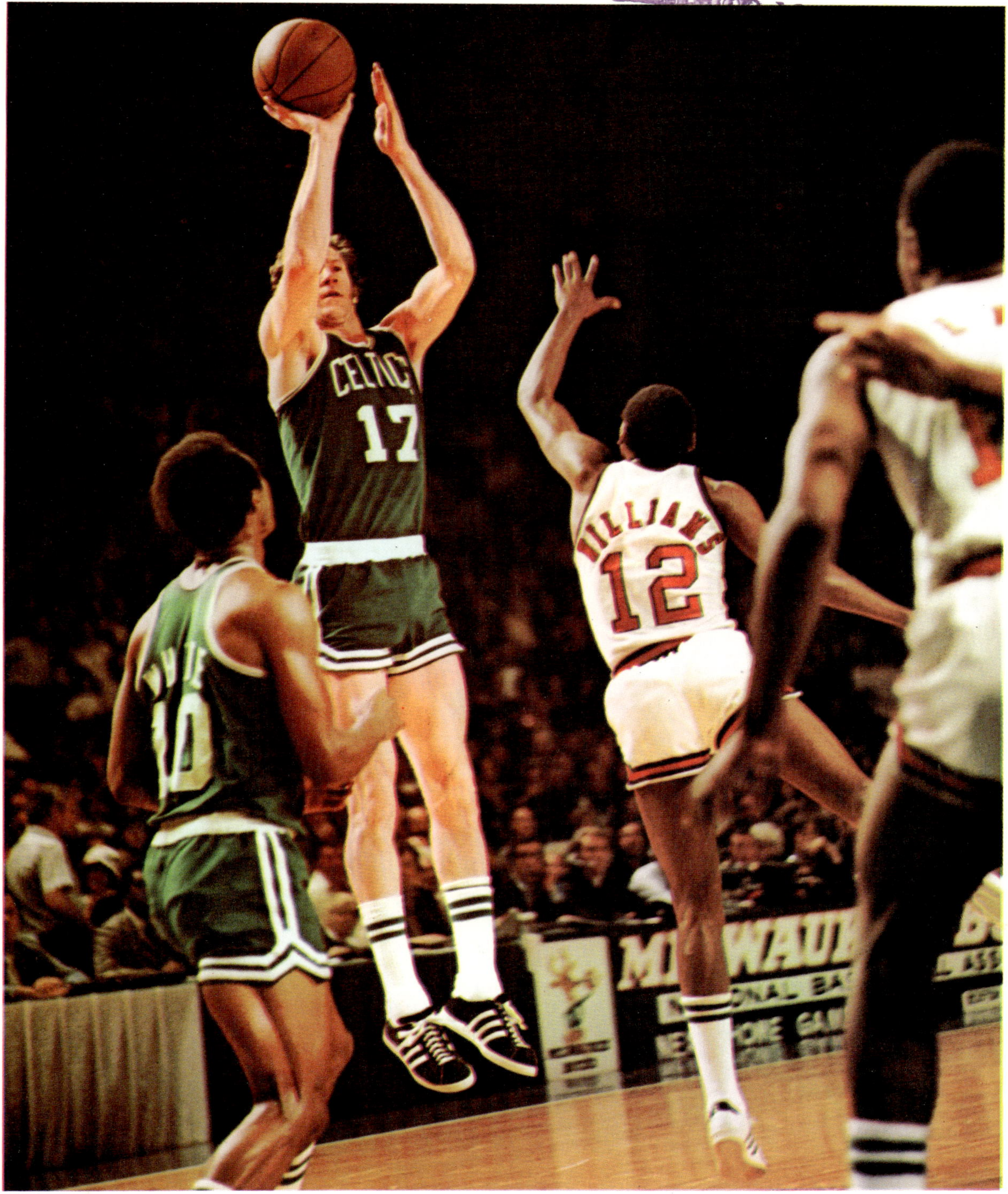
17
WILLIAMS
12

2
Thwunk! The Dunk!

The first time Arty Jones started thinking seriously about basketball was the first time he ever dunked a ball.

Before that, it was just another game. Just another way to have some fun, passing the time with the guys.

Arty was never that excited about sports. He was never that excited about school. He played at them both because they were the only games in town.

In the neighborhood where Arty grew up, all the people were working people — maintenance men, gardeners, domestic help, tradesmen, a few small contractors. People who worked with their hands and bent their backs. Like Arty says, most everybody on the block wore a blue or green uniform with his name over the pocket. The average income was around three thousand dollars. Twice that, maybe, if your mother worked, too.

There was enough money so that nobody went hungry. But there wasn't much more.

In his early years, Arty spent a lot of time by himself. He was a loner. He sat home a lot. He entertained himself while his three brothers were on the street, running with the crowd. A lot of the time, Arty would read — anything he could lay his hands on that told

13

him something about the world outside Miami. He read comic books, old mail-order catalogues, tattered copies of *Boys' Life*, even a school book once in a while, when he found one that interested him. He didn't start hanging around with the gang until he started getting interested in sports. He remembers walking over to the high school in the afternoons to watch football practice with some of his friends. They all thought the shoulder pads were part of the people.

Arty was eight years old the first time he picked up a basketball. He was sitting on a curb in front of an abandoned building a block from his house. Some older kids were playing there, shooting the ball at a rusty hoop they had nailed to a telephone pole. One of them overshot the hoop from the side. The ball rolled over by Arty's feet. He picked it up, gave it a pump toward the hoop with a two-handed push shot, and missed by ten feet.

It wasn't long after that he started playing regularly with the older kids. The games weren't organized. They'd just all get together on a Saturday morning or after school and head on over to the playground to "toss 'em up." Sometimes they'd shoot over at the high school, until the older guys showed up and chased them off. Often, they'd be back in front of the abandoned house, shooting at the crooked hoop on the telephone pole.

Arty was in the sixth grade when he first played organized ball. The grade school had a team and the coach taught some fundamentals — how to shoot a lay-up, how to dribble, how to pass, and a dozen more. By this time, Arty was beginning to stretch out — tall and skinny, with great big, long feet that used to get in his way. Whenever they chose up sides for a game, Arty was among the first picked.

The years between grade school and the end

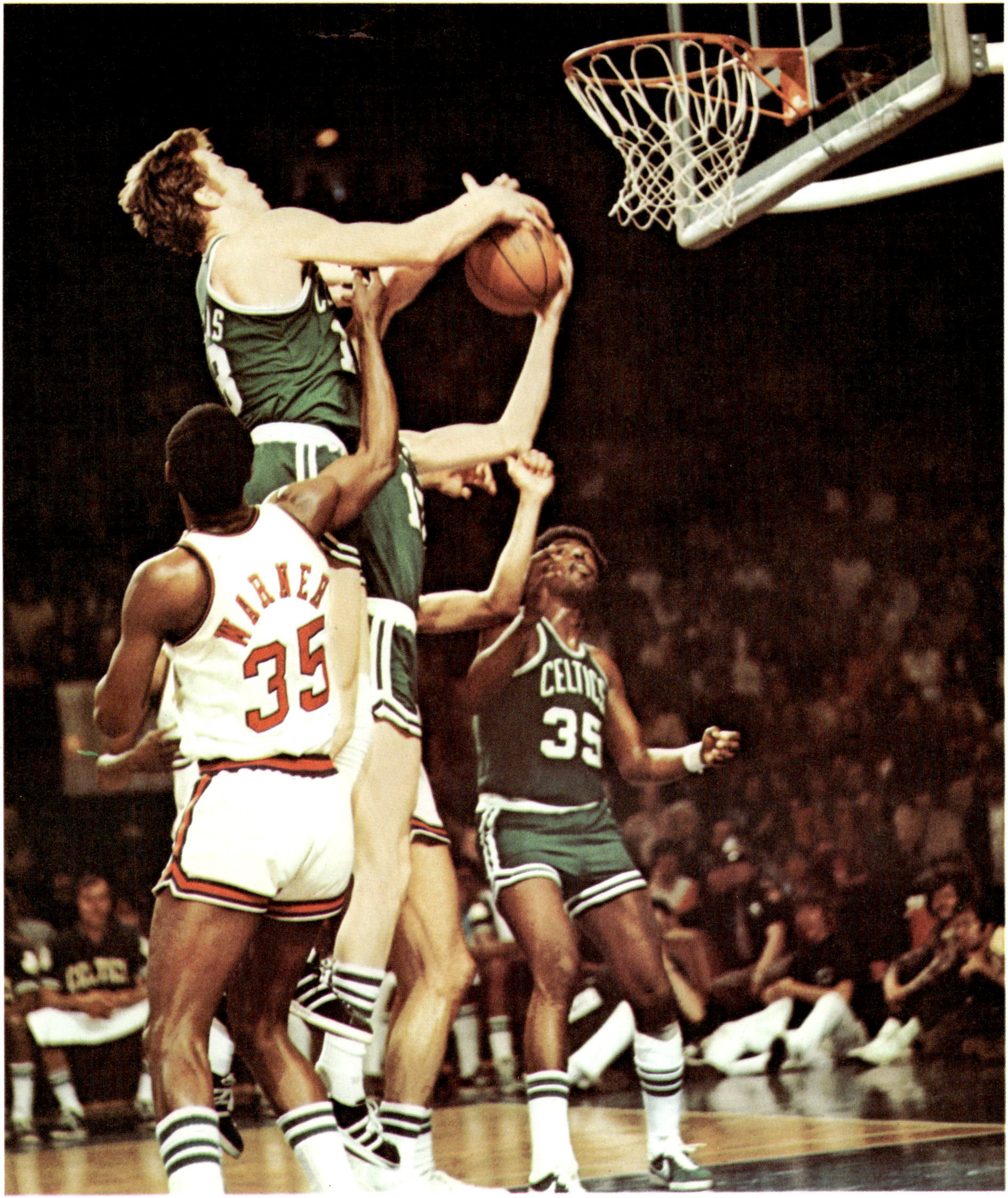
WARNER
35
CELTICS
35

of junior high were the years when Arty started noticing that he had some real talent. He had that size advantage. He was starting to develop a pretty fair shot. And he could leap.

The coaches saw it, too. And by the time he was in the ninth grade, tall and skinny Artemus Jones was beginning to turn some heads. Some of the older fans around the neighborhood were starting to say that Arty Jones was a comer. He was going to help the school.

The school had a way of winning. No matter how bad the football team was, everybody knew that come winter, the basketball team would be making a run for the state title. Everyone connected with the team had pride and confidence. Anyone good enough to make the varsity considered it an honor. The players were heroes.

One night after the regular practice, Arty was getting in some extra practice. He was over in a corner of the gym, dribbling some, "throwin' 'em up." He heard a voice yell out over in the stands.

"Hey, Jones, let's see a dunk! You're big enough to dunk."

Arty looked around. It was Wilbur Peabody, the first trumpet in the band.

"Go ahead, Jones," yelled Wilbur. "Let's see you try it. Drop it in there!"

So Arty dropped it in there.

His hands weren't big enough to palm a regulation ball — they still aren't — but this ball was a softy, a cheapo. It had just enough air pumped in to make it bounce. It was soft enough that he could dig into it with one hand.

He started his run back by the free-throw line. He built up a good head of steam and took off through the air. He arched toward the basket as high as he could leap. He gave

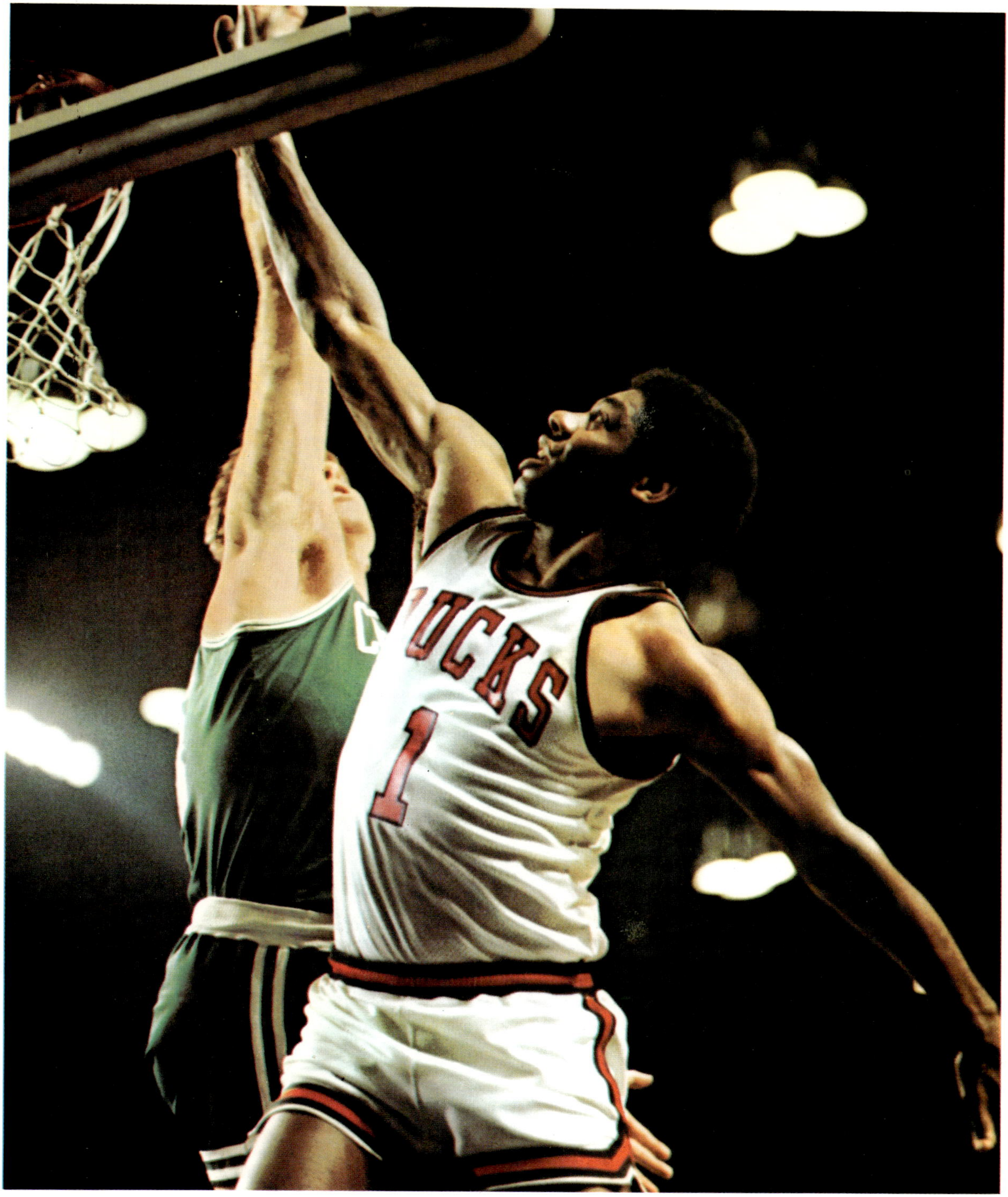
UCKS
1

the ball an upward boost with his left hand and stretched his right arm as far above the rim as he could. Then he slammed it home.

Thwunk! The Dunk!

Wilbur Peabody was pleased with himself. "I told you so, man. I knew you were big enough to dunk, just from lookin' at you."

But Arty hardly heard him. Arty was too excited to listen. He was all caught up in the rush. A door had just opened to a whole new thing.

"Whoo-ie!" thought Arty, "I can dunk! Do you believe that? I can dunk!" He dunked again. And again. And again. . . .

From that time on, for the next six years, basketball for Arty Jones was a whole new ball game.

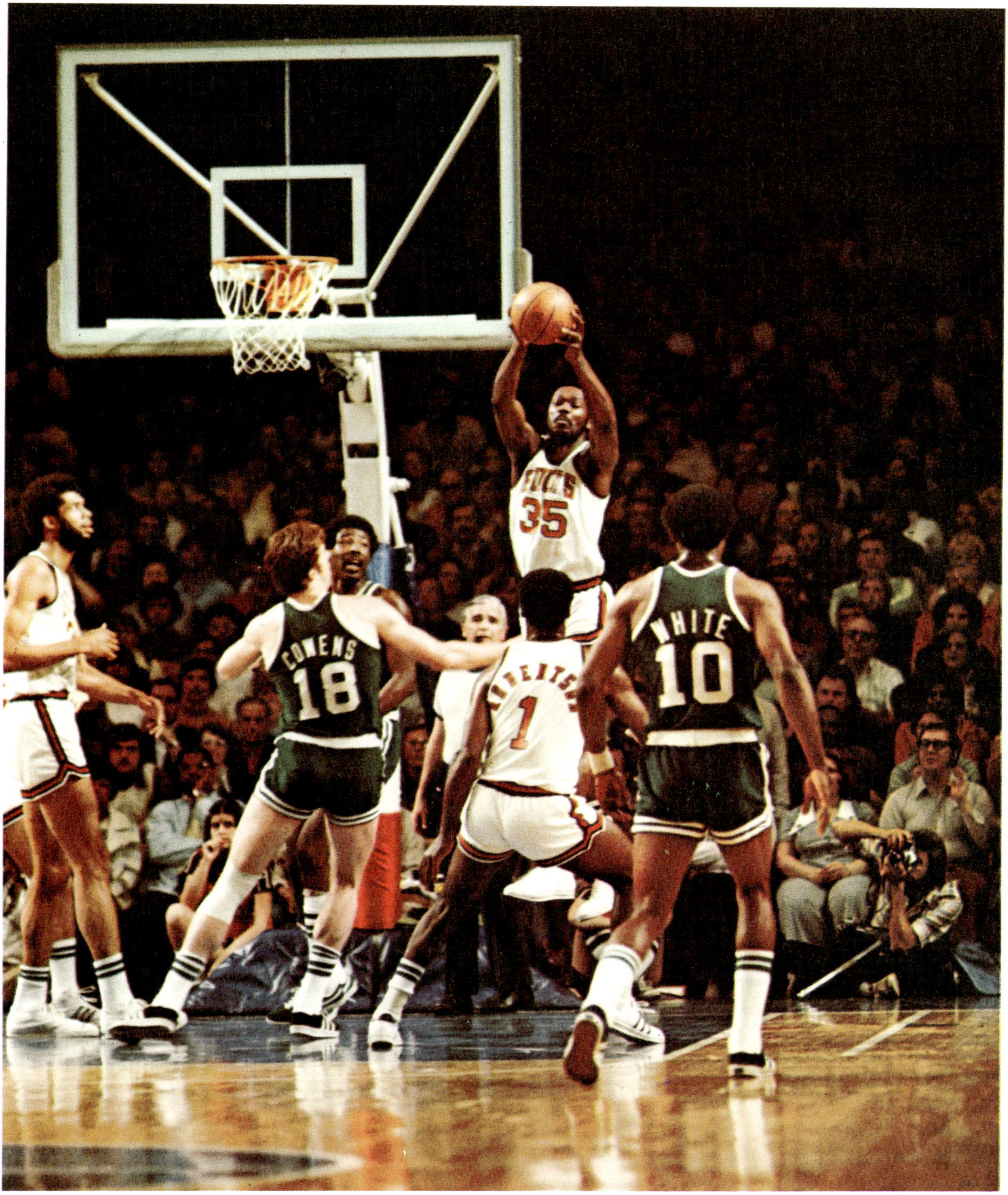
35
COWENS
18
1
WHITE
10

3
More Than Just Fun

"So you're telling me that's when you started taking it seriously?" asks Monte McCoy. He and Arty are crossing the street from the restaurant to the Arena. It is fifteen minutes before the game. A cold spring rain is falling. Hundreds of fans are hurrying through the sprinkle, jostling each other for places in the long line streaming through the doors.

"Well, that's about the time it started being something more than just fun," says Arty. "I mean, it was still fun and all. But there was more to it than just horsin' around in the schoolyard with the guys.

"I mean, way back when I was playin' with the junior varsity, I knew that someday I was going to be on 'the team.' But it was the dunk that told me I could do something that most everybody else can't.

"Man, there for a few weeks I'd dunk anything I could get my hands on — tennis balls, volley balls, paper cups. Pretty soon I got to where I could drop a regulation ball. It was about then that I started workin' on some other stuff, too, like ball control.

"I remember this one ol' dude tellin' me, 'You got to be able to handle the ball. You got to be able to control it.' I really hadn't thought about it much, playin' under the

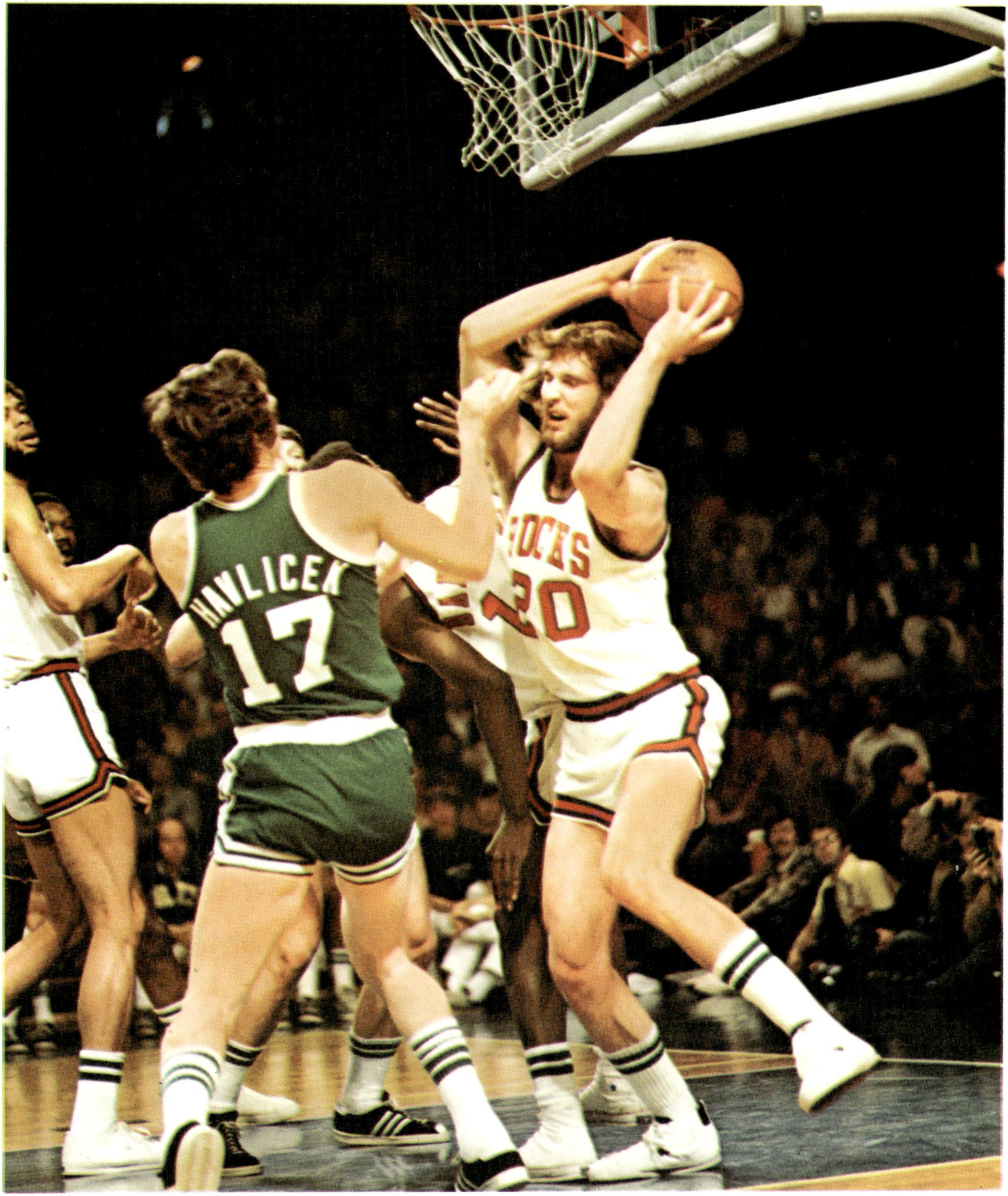
HAVLICEK
17
BUCKS
20

basket most of the time. But I went and did it anyway, 'cause that's what somebody older said I was supposed to do.

"Sometimes, you know, folks know what they're talkin' about when they tell you how you should live, and sometimes they don't. Sometimes you got to go and try it out yourself so that you know the difference."

So Arty Jones began to work at it a little. He knew he had a few things working in his favor and he began to take advantage of them. In time, Arty became a basketball star. In time, he became the team's leading scorer and rebounder. Part of the reason was the high school coach, Allen J. Winthrop. Allen J. Winthrop was the kind of man the players wanted to put out for.

He was a large man, six feet four inches and 240 pounds, a tackle on his college football team. He had played a little semi-professional football. At Arty's school, he taught physical education and coached the line in football. He was tough but sensitive, strong but gentle, demanding but understanding. He was the kind of man who acted like he cared about the kids he coached. In turn, the kids cared about him. They worked hard to please him.

"We used to run these wind sprints in practice," Arty recalls. "We'd go up and down the gym, with Allen J. sendin' us on our way. Sometimes he'd run along with us. He was pretty quick for a big man.

"If you knew ol' Allen J. was keepin' up with you, you'd step out just a little bit quicker. That's how we got in shape.

"It paid off in the games. We'd run most everybody right into the court because we were always in better condition.

"I had this thing I'd do maybe once or twice a game. I'd haul down a rebound, and if the other team was draggin', layin' back, I'd take off on the run. I'd catch 'em goin' back-

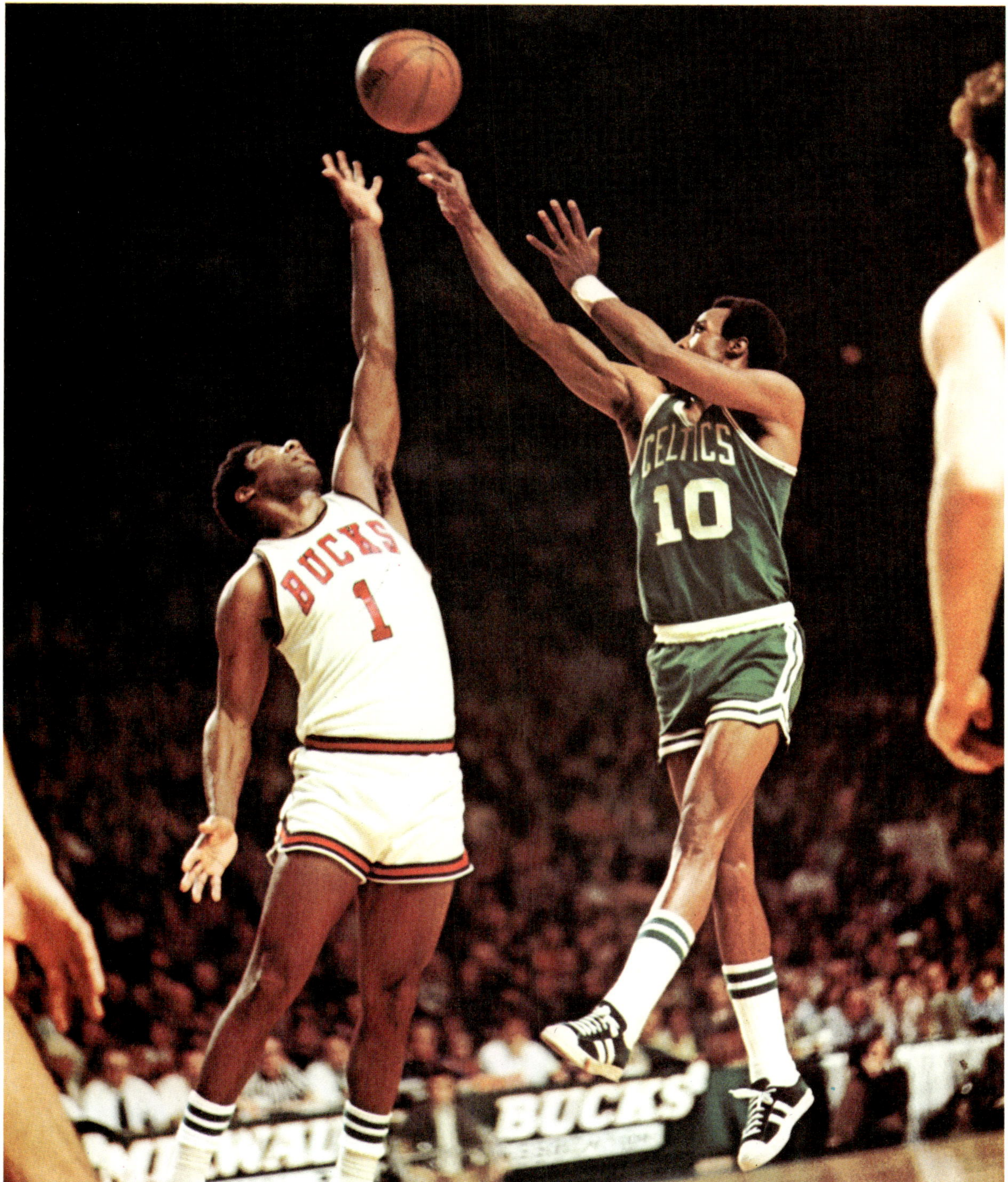
CELTICS
10
BUCKS
1
BUCKS

wards, and it was no trick at all to fake one way and go the other. Then I'd drive in and give 'em the dunk, turn, and keep right on runnin', all the way back to defense.

"The crowd would go crazy — they always liked that move. Allen J. would be up off the bench clappin'. And the other coach, well, he'd be mad! He'd be yellin' at his boys to get with it — beseechin' 'em, we used to say.

"It was great times. I loved it, man.

"Allen J. had another way about him, too. If we were fallin' down on defense, and if our man was beatin' us on the boards, Allen J. would call time out and call us all over. He'd take us aside and put his arms around our shoulders, and he'd say, 'Arty, Arty — now what's happenin' out there, Arty? That boy is five inches shorter than you and you mean to say that you can't block him out? Tell me that ain't so, Arty. Tell me you can beat that man. If you can't, you just say so and I'll understand.'

"And sure enough, we'd get to feelin' ashamed of ourselves and we'd say, 'Yeah, Coach, I can beat that man.' And we'd go out and beat him. Allen J. had a way of tellin' you what you already should know, and then gettin' you to do it."

Arty and Monte are nearing the press table at courtside of the Arena. The Bucks and the Celtics are running through their warm-ups.

"Yeah, ol' Allen J. was somethin' else — still is, too. I still stop off and see him when I'm back down home."

By the time Arty was a senior, he knew that if he wanted it, he was going to get an athletic scholarship to college. It was something that everybody just knew — who was good enough to go on, and who wasn't going to make it. On his playing ability, Arty knew he had a good chance. As far as his grades went — well, they weren't all that

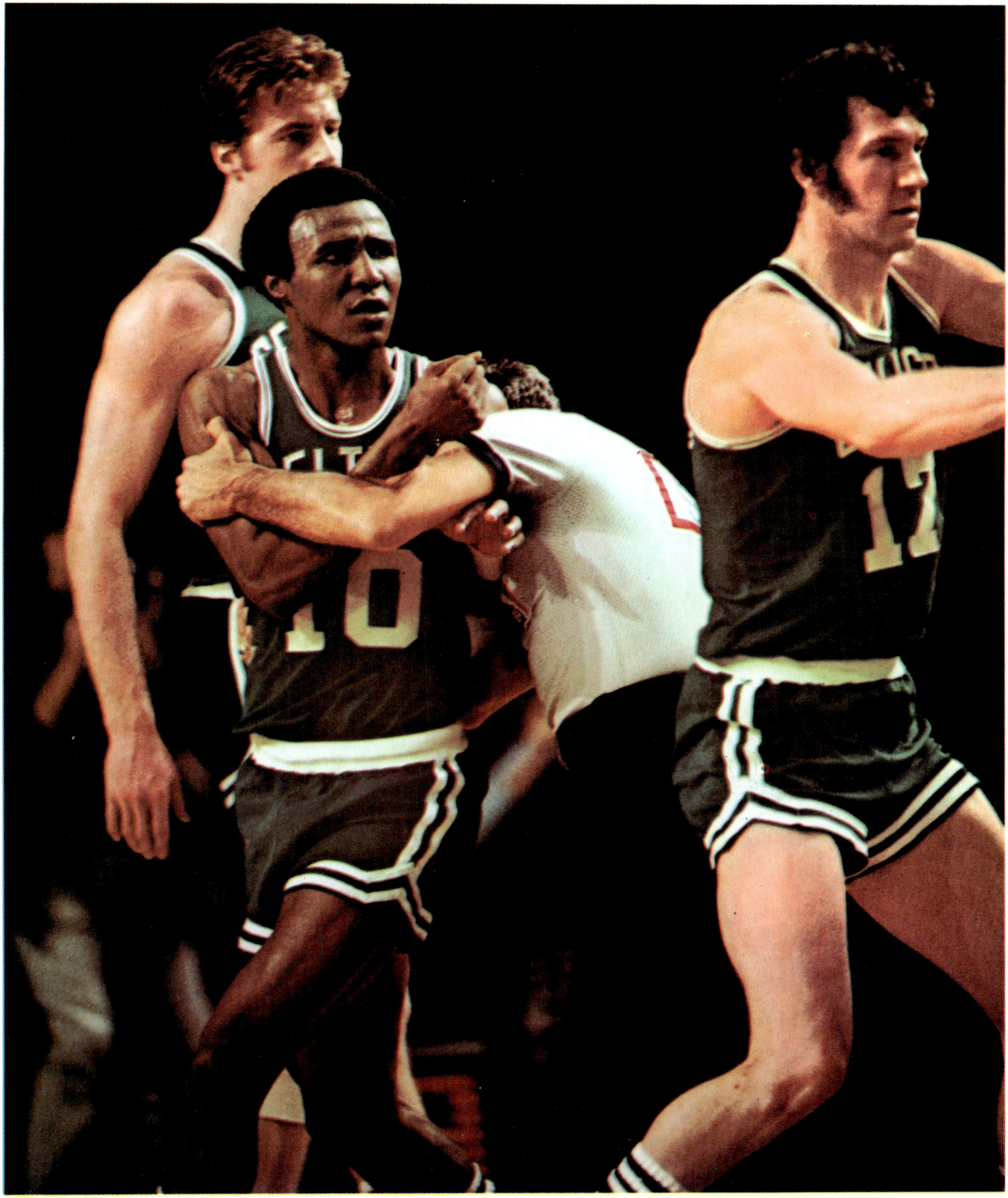

good. But then they weren't all that bad, either.

The courses that interested him pulled him up. They made up for the bad ones that he didn't care so much about, the ones he didn't work at. With all that reading he'd done over the years, he knew a little bit about a lot of things. Maybe not enough to be among the better students, but enough to get him by. The college offers started coming in.

Up to then, all of the players from Arty's school who had gone off to college had gone to black schools in the South. Some went to Fisk, some went to Florida A. & M., some to Grambling or Tennessee State or Arkansas A.M. & N. Red McLellen went to A.M. & N.

The only one who had gone somewhere different was Leon Hayes. Hayes had gone to Bradley, in Peoria, Illinois. He was the first player to come out of the school and go up North to a "white" college. When the stories about Leon drifted back down to Miami, Arty was listening. Leon Hayes had done something new, and Arty wanted to go the same way.

He got the chance. There was an alumnus in Miami from a big state college in New England. The man kept an eye out for high school ballplayers he thought could make it. He watched Arty play a few times, and he got on the telephone and called the coach. He told him there was a kid in Miami who could help him out. The coach called back and talked to Arty, inviting him to fly up on the next plane and have a look around. Arty did. When he saw the campus and the town and thought about the chance he had that most of the people he knew would never have, he made his decision fast.

Arty Jones was going to college to play basketball, and he was going to do it at a big, famous college. He felt good.

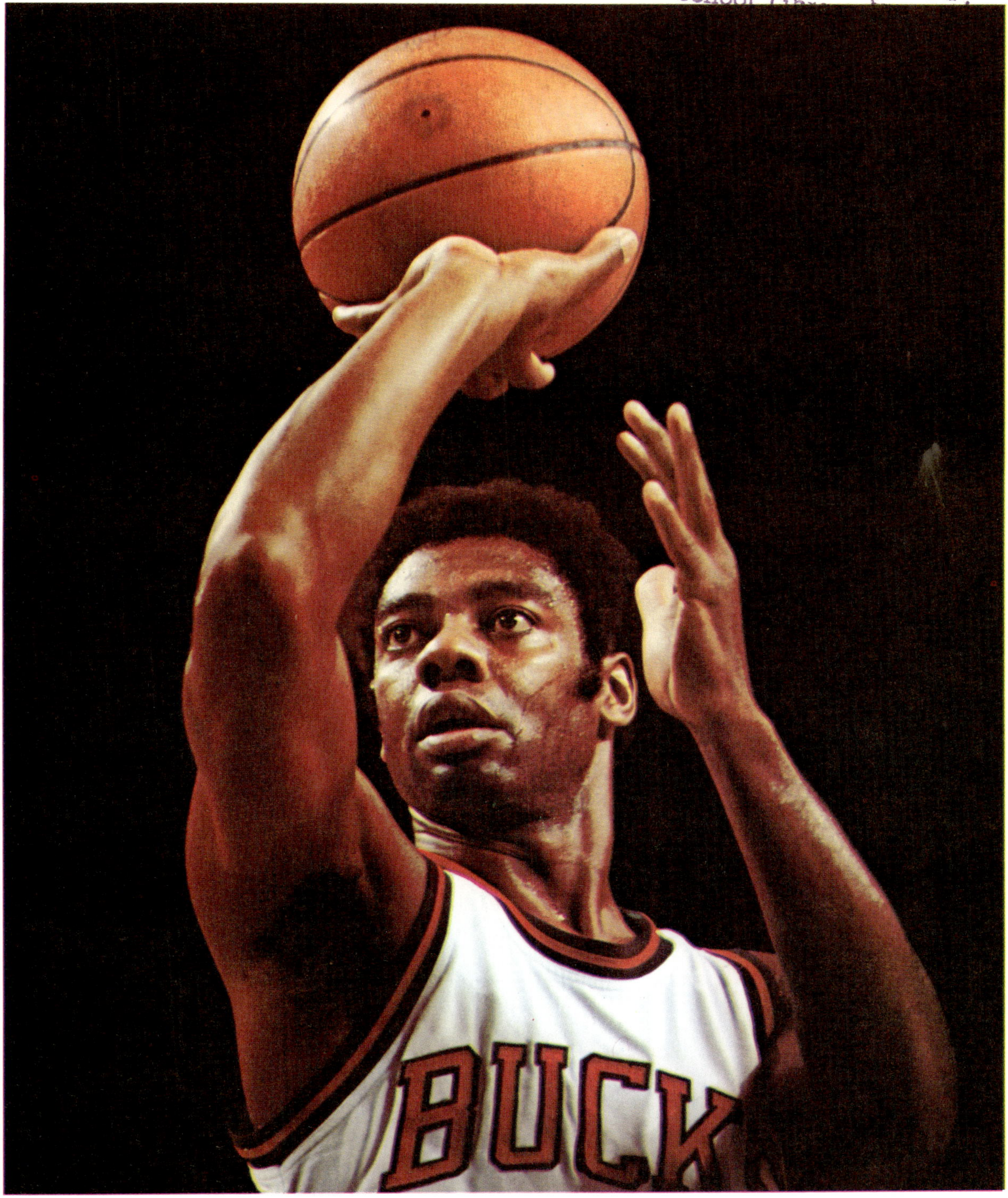
BUCK

4
Talent And Hard Work

There are several ways to look at basketball. One of them is to take it seriously. Another is to take it for what it's worth — to consider it as a game.

Arty Jones has seen it both ways. Tonight, sitting there behind his typewriter at the press table, he's taking it a little more seriously than usual. Three hours from now, when the game is over, the Celtics or the Bucks will walk off the court champion of the National Basketball Association. It's the climax of a long, long season.

When he thinks about how much time and energy these men have put into their game, Arty has a real sense of appreciation. On one hand, he knows they're in there for the money. But on the other, he knows they earn it. The average salary in the NBA is $92,000. Of course, they don't all make that much. Some of the benchwarmers are down around $25,000 a year. But the high-salaried players, like Kareem Abdul-Jabbar or Walt Frazier, make enough extra to jack the average up.

But, thinks Arty, nobody is worth $92,000 a year for bouncing a ball. Especially when millions of people are sweating to make enough to eat and keep a roof over their heads. That just isn't right.

29

Basketball players *do* work hard, though.

Their season starts at training camp in September. It runs through eighty-two regular season games and a few exhibitions. And if a team is good enough to make it through the playoffs, the grind isn't over until May. That's a lot of miles on a man's legs.

Take John Havlicek there. Havlicek is an all-star forward/guard and he's a hustler. He runs four or five miles a game, and he runs hard. He figures that over the length of his career, he's probably run around the world.

Then you have to consider the travel, the time it takes to get from one city to another. The time that's spent waiting in airports at one o'clock in the morning for a flight from Buffalo to Los Angeles for a game the next afternoon. Maybe after that, it's back to Phoenix for another game the next night or on to San Francisco or Seattle.

And when there's time to kill, which is more often than the players would like, they kill it at a movie or lounging in a hotel lobby. Sometimes they kill it cooped up in a hotel room, catching up on sleep or watching the game shows on television. They live out of a suitcase and they live on food from hotels and restaurants. After a while, it all tastes pretty much the same.

It's a first class group, thinks Arty, two hundred men who play basketball well enough to play it in the NBA. There's all kinds of good ballplayers in this country — on playgrounds, in driveways, in YMCA gyms — but only two hundred of them have made it to the top.

They make it on their talent and hard work. Professional basketball players are incredibly skilled, their reactions are superb. But they've all paid their dues. None of them got where they are by accident. All of them had to put some time and effort into it.

Sure, they might get caught loafing some

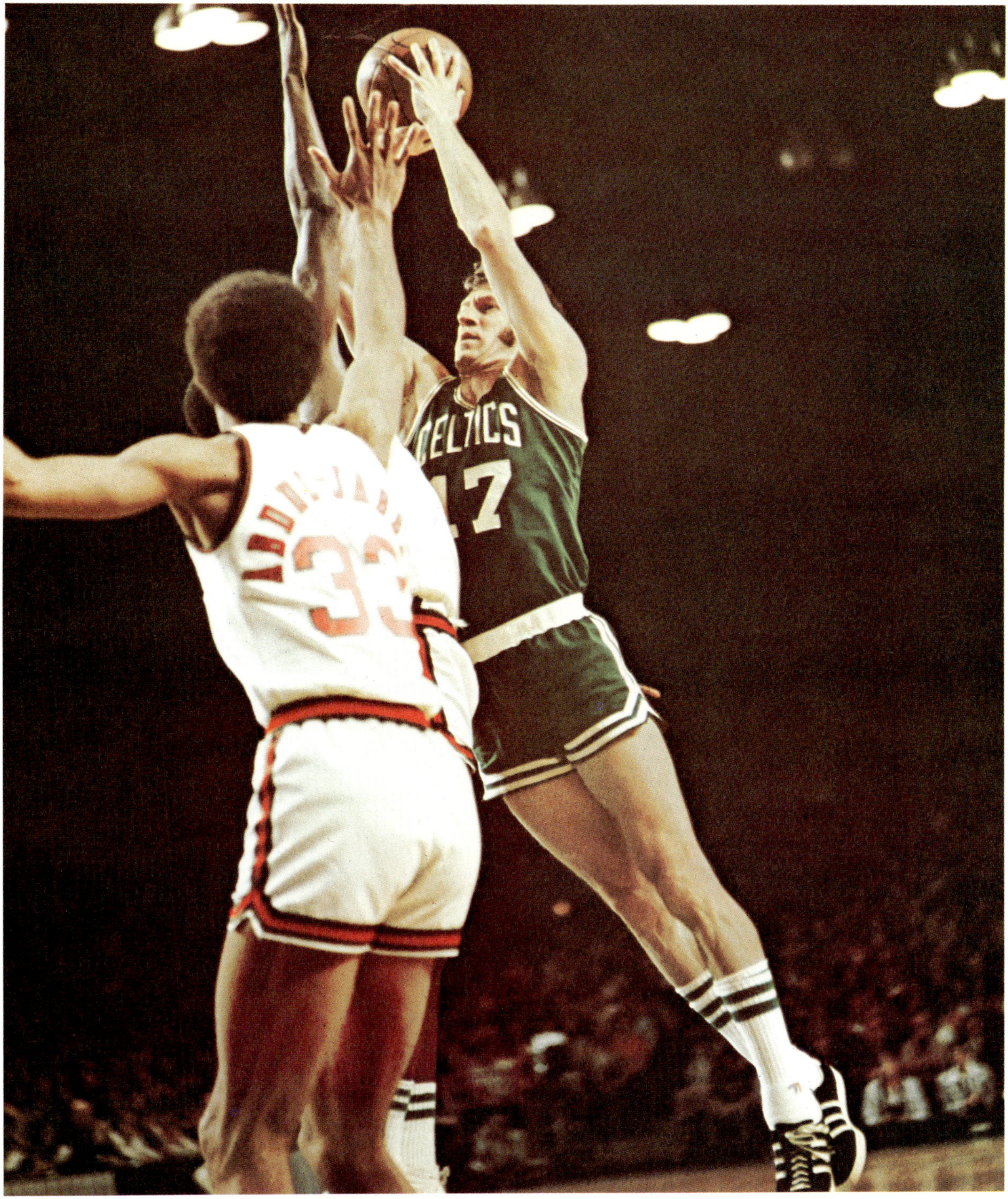

during that long season, usually when they're playing one of the weaker teams. But when it comes time for the big game, when the honors and reputations are on the line, you know they're giving it all they have.

Like the Celtics and the Bucks tonight. They're high. They're up for it. Emotion is soaring, and the second effort is second nature.

Tonight, they're taking it all for real.

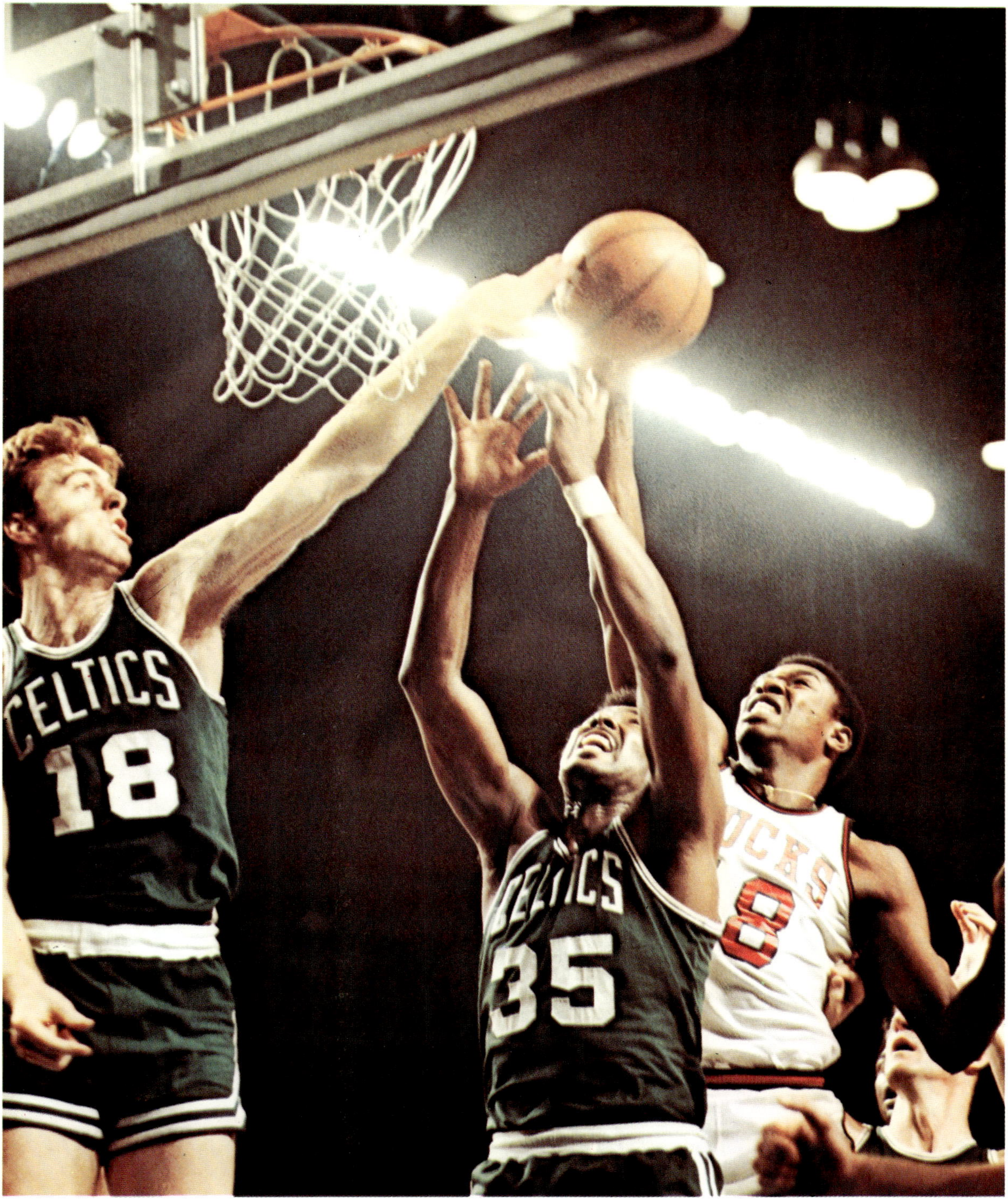
CELTICS
18
CELTICS
35
UCKS
8

5
In A Jam

The Bucks are in a jam. It's midway through the first quarter and the Celtics are working up a big lead. That's mainly because they've shut the Bucks off.

Defense has always been their strong point, thinks Arty. Way back when he was a kid, it was defense that made them go. He remembers Elgin Baylor, the great Los Angeles Laker forward, probably the first superstar he followed closely. Baylor had all the moves; he was a scoring machine. Yet he was never enough by himself to carry the Lakers past Boston's rugged defense. Red Auerbach coached that defense, and Russell made it work.

The Celtics were hurting for the next five years because they didn't have a big center strong enough to hold off the other NBA big men, like Kareem and Wilt Chamberlain and Nate Thurmond. In the NBA, you've got to have an outstanding big man. Until the Celtics found themselves another one, they were just another team.

They found their big man in Dave Cowens, a six-foot-nine-inch redhead whose attitude is play as hard as you can, and when you get tired, play harder. At six feet nine, Cowens is nowhere near the biggest man in the league, but he plays like a man who is seven feet

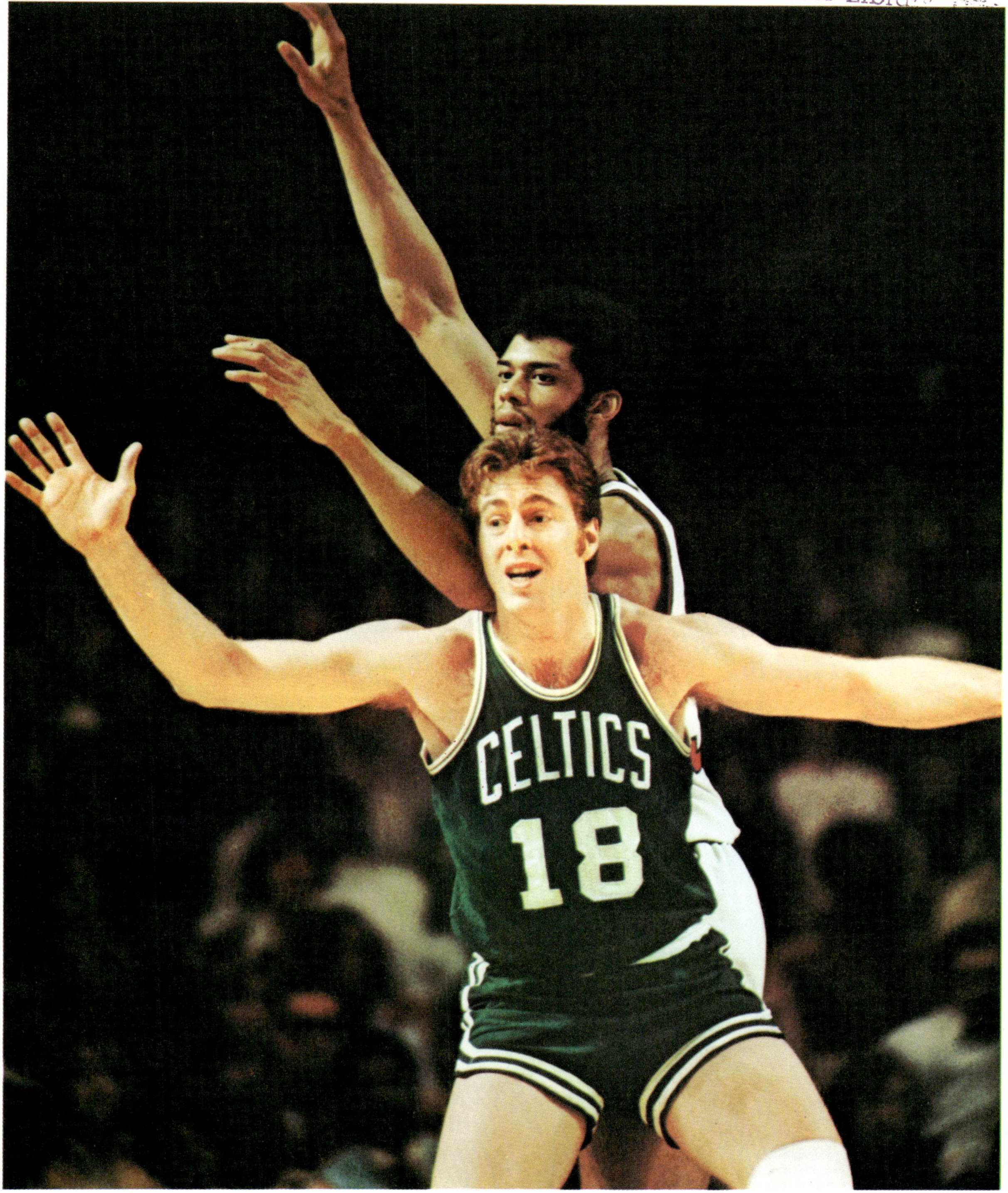
CELTICS
18

three. He is one of those guys who gives 110 percent.

Arty watches him block a shot by Kareem, who may be seven inches taller. There aren't many players in the NBA who can block a shot by Kareem Abdul-Jabbar. Kareem, one-on-one, is as good as they'll ever come. But up against Big Red Cowens, he's going to have to extend himself.

If Cowens can keep up the pressure, the Celtics will win. If he can hold Kareem down with help from Havlicek and Don Nelson and Paul Silas, Boston's big forwards, the Celts will ride. As long as they keep sagging on Kareem, double- and triple-teaming him, it's going to be up to the rest of the Bucks to pull it out.

If it's up to the rest of the Bucks tonight, thinks Arty, scratching some notes on his pad, they're not going to make it.

The Bucks are a one-man gang. The gang is Kareem Abdul-Jabbar. Everything they do is set up for Kareem. If he can score, they have a chance, even if the rest of them are having only an average game. But Kareem has got to get his thirty points, and he's got to get his fifteen rebounds. At his best, he's almost good enough to win it by himself.

The rest of the Bucks aren't bad, but they go only as far as Kareem takes them. Bobby Dandridge, one of the forwards, has hot shooting nights. Tonight isn't one of them. He's been off and on during the whole series. And tonight he's off.

Dandridge isn't a big, strong forward. That keeps him from muscling in under the boards to help Kareem with the rebounds, so here the Bucks have Cornell Warner and Curtis Perry. Both Warner and Perry are strong rebounders, but neither one of them is much of a shooter. Tonight they're having more trouble with their shots than usual. The Celtics' front line has them bottled up.

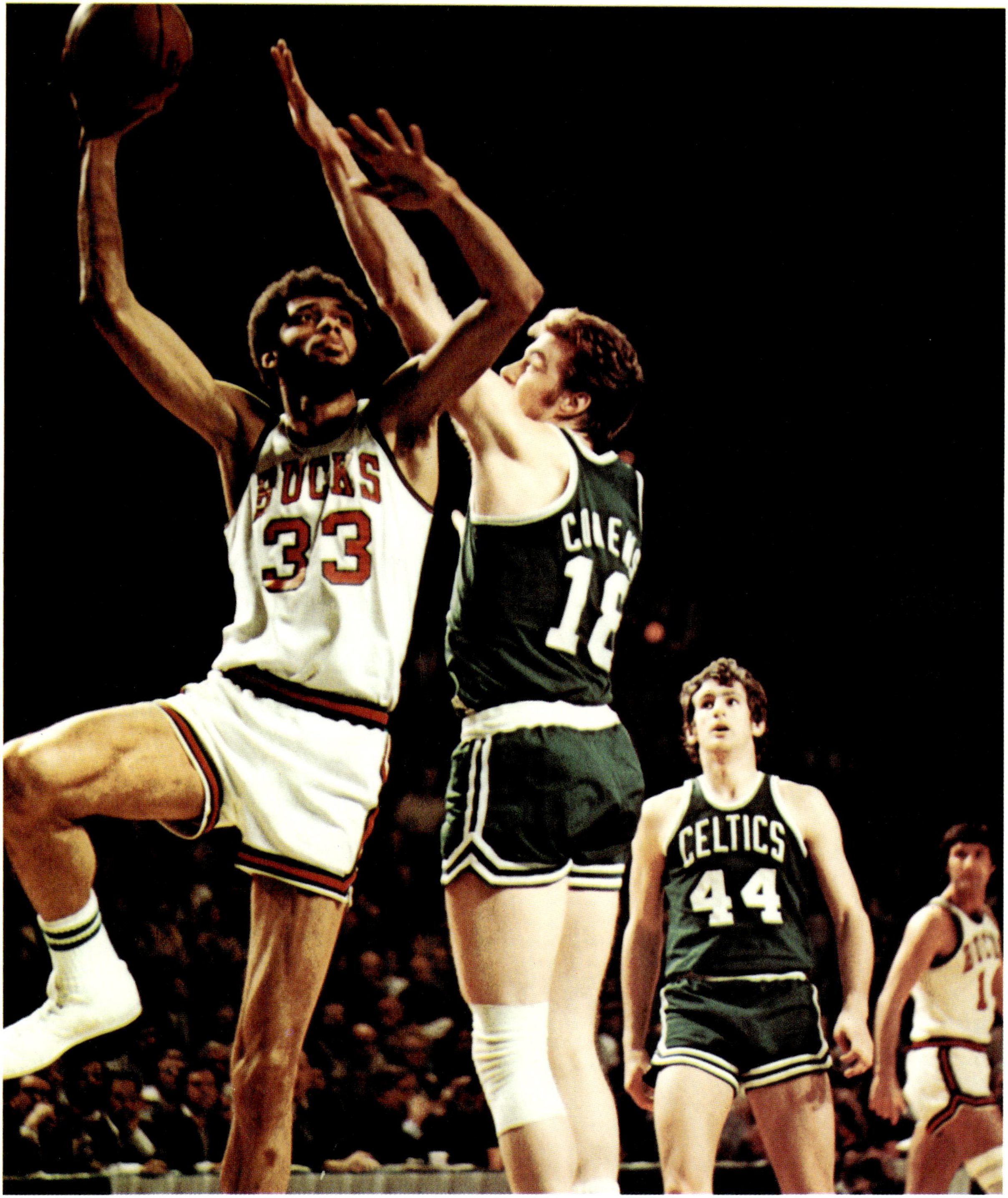
BUCKS
33
CELTICS
44

In the front line, it's come down to Kareem against the crowd. Right now he's losing to the odds.

For the Bucks, it's not much better in the backcourt. Their best guard, Lucius Allen, hasn't played in weeks because of a foot injury. With Allen in the lineup, the Bucks might still have a chance. Without him, it's very doubtful.

Jon McGlocklin is hurt, too. He has a painful leg injury, but he's suited up because there just isn't enough help to go around. When he's healthy, McGlocklin can shoot from outside as well as anyone. But tonight he's playing on one leg.

To beef up the backcourt, Larry Costello has put in Mickey Davis at guard. Davis is normally a forward, a castoff from the American Basketball Association. He has been the Bucks' sixth man all season. He has done his job well, but now he's a bit out of his range. In the NBA, unless your name is Havlicek, you just don't switch positions in a championship series and get away with it clean. But Davis is holding his own.

Then there's Oscar Robertson. On paper, thinks Arty, Oscar is Milwaukee's other superstar. Oscar is the man who takes the pressure off Kareem and sets him up to do his best. On paper, they are some combination. But on the court, especially in this series, Oscar Robertson is not the player he used to be.

It's kind of a shame, thinks Arty, but that's how it goes when the years catch up with you. He remembers Oscar during all those seasons with the Cincinnati Royals, when he was the best guard in the game. Maybe the best guard ever.

Oscar Robertson is thirty-five years old. In any other job but professional sports, he'd be in his prime. But in pro basketball, at thirty-five, he's just about through. His legs can't take it anymore.

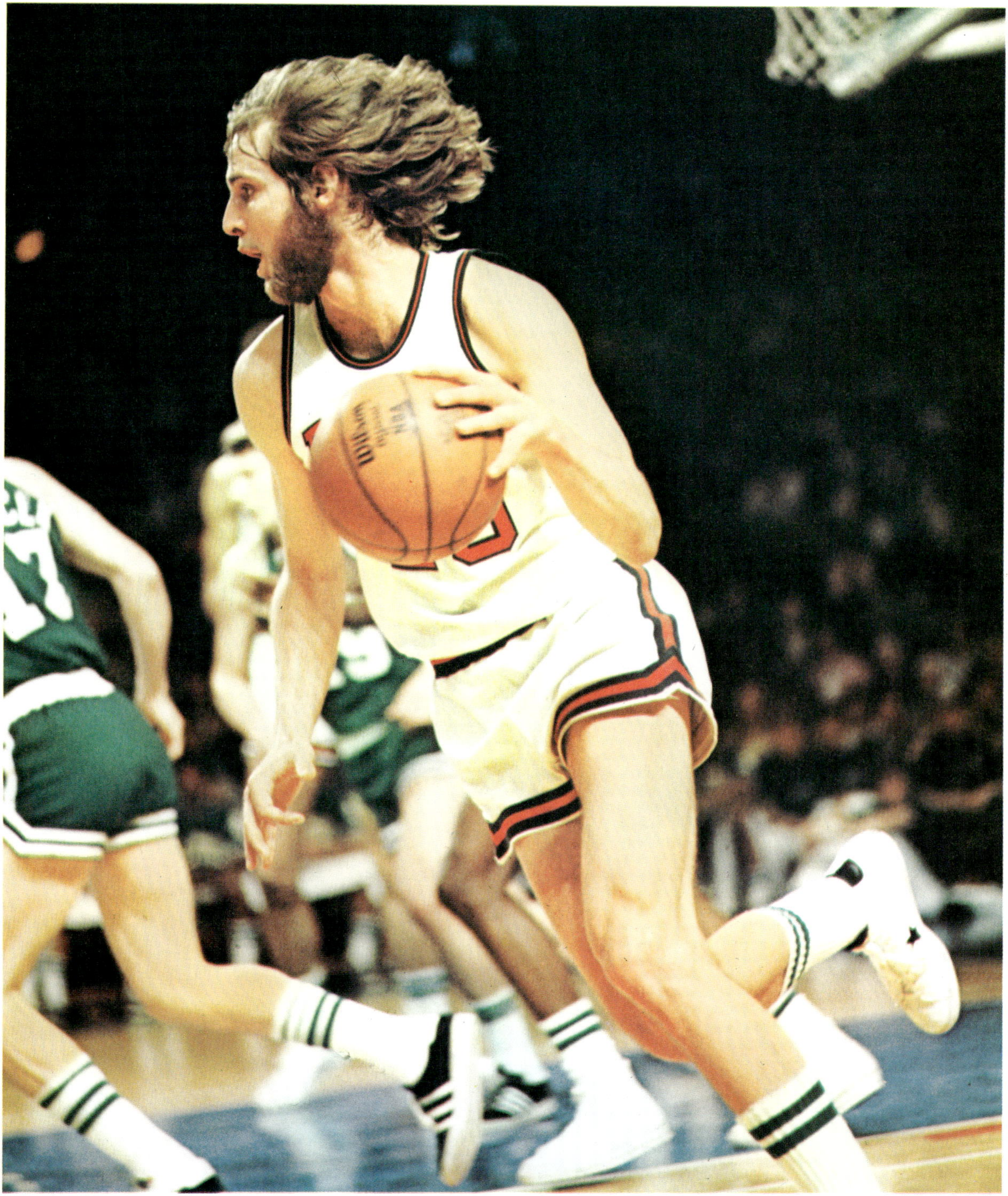

And speed, tonight, is one thing the Bucks need. Oscar has been hounded by young Don Chaney and Jo Jo White, and he's been struggling to get the ball up court, struggling to get it in to Kareem in the post. With Allen out and McGlocklin hampered, with Davis playing an unfamiliar position, the burden rests on Oscar. The Celtics know this, and they're making him work for every inch of floor he covers. Oscar is showing the strain.

The scoreboard is showing the result. The halftime buzzer sounds and Boston has the Bucks down by thirteen points. The odds on a comeback are slim.

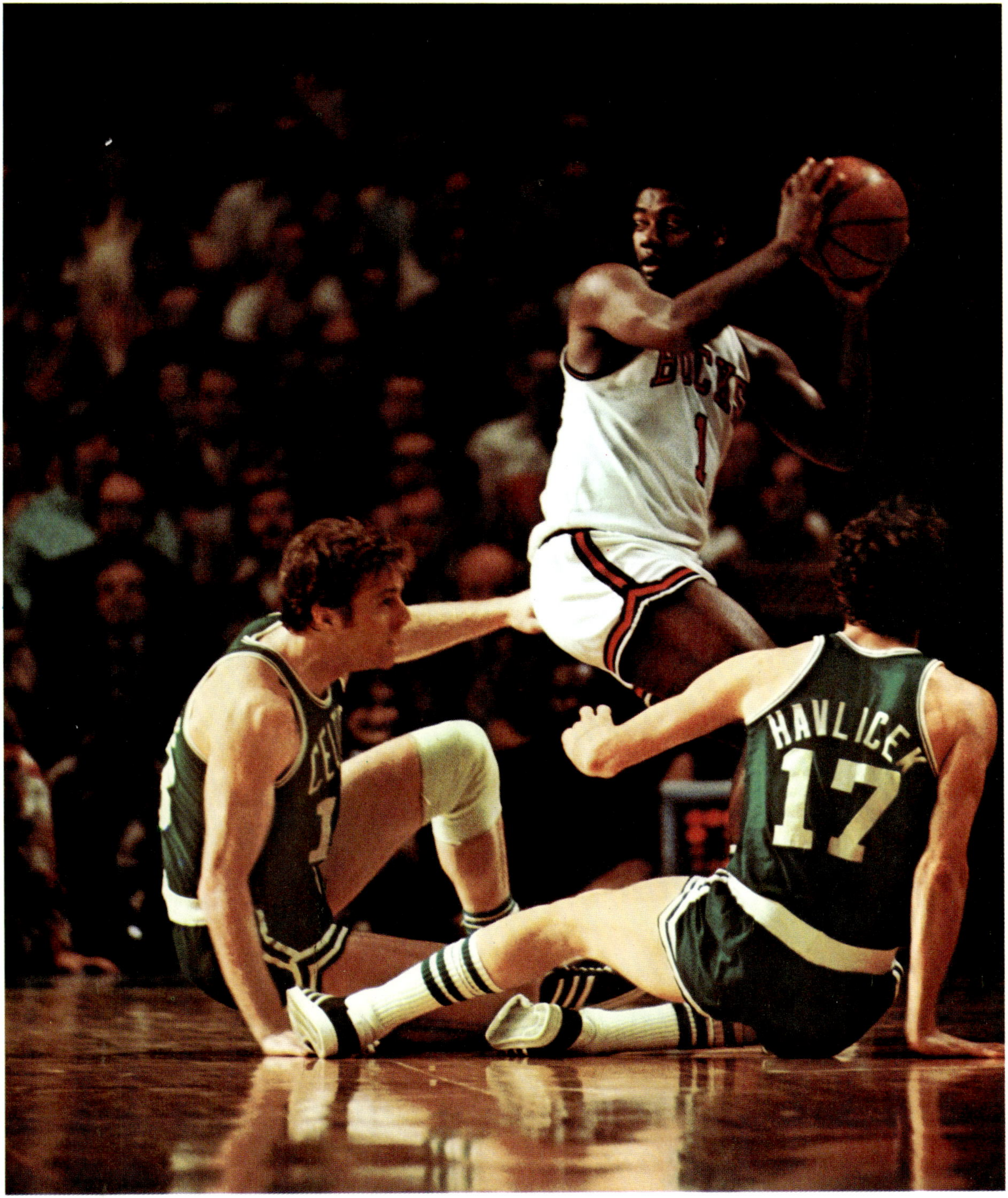
BUCKS
1
HAVLICEK
17

6
A Whole Different Thing

Arty Jones slides into the press hospitality room and moves past a cluster of jabbering sportswriters to the cooler. He fishes out a cold drink and cracks open the can, helping himself to a ham sandwich from the table. He looks around the room. Even if he didn't know most of them, it wouldn't be hard to tell the Boston reporters from the local bunch.

The Boston writers are resting on the Celtics' thirteen-point lead. They are all smiles and jokes and laughter. The local writers look like they have lost a good friend.

Sportswriters are supposed to be objective, but they usually aren't. When you cover a team for any length of time, thinks Arty, you get to taking the wins and losses personally. It's much more fun to write a story about a big win than it is to write about a big loss. When the team you cover loses a lot, the writing becomes work.

A tall, thin man with a balding head taps Arty on the shoulder. It is Ralph Petzer, the sports editor of the *Gazette*.

"Well, Jones," says Petzer, "it's looking pretty bleak for our boys, pretty bleak." Petzer is wearing a long face. "It's going to be a long ride home."

43

"Don't take it so personal, Ralph," laughs Arty. "You'll still get home. Have another sandwich and forget about it. There's always next year, you know."

Petzer gives him a shake of the head. "I don't know about you, Jones, I just don't know about you. Sometimes I think you're in the wrong business. You got no spirit."

In walks Monte McCoy. He grabs a cold drink and weaves his way through the crowd to Arty's side.

"The Bucks are dead," says Monte.

"Looks that way," says Arty. "Get good pictures?"

"The usual," says Monte. "A good Kareem dunk shot. One of Oscar falling down, with Chaney stealing the ball. And I caught some good bench shots, too — Costello is suffering and Tommy Heinsohn is looking like a hound dog. He's got a thirteen-point lead and he's frowning."

"He always looks like that," says Arty. "Coaches are always grim. You know that."

Monte spears a doughnut from the table.

"So then what happened?"

"Huh?"

"What happened in college?"

"Oh, yeah, college," says Arty. "College was all right but the basketball wasn't. It was a whole different thing, man. I mean, all of a sudden it was a business."

His first afternoon in the dorm, Arty Jones was lonesome. Homesick. He sat there on his unmade bed in his little room, and counted out his money. He had sixty dollars to his name, and the price of a one-way ticket back to Miami was forty-eight dollars. He had just hung up the phone to the bus station when George Richland walked in the door.

George Richland was the coach. He was a

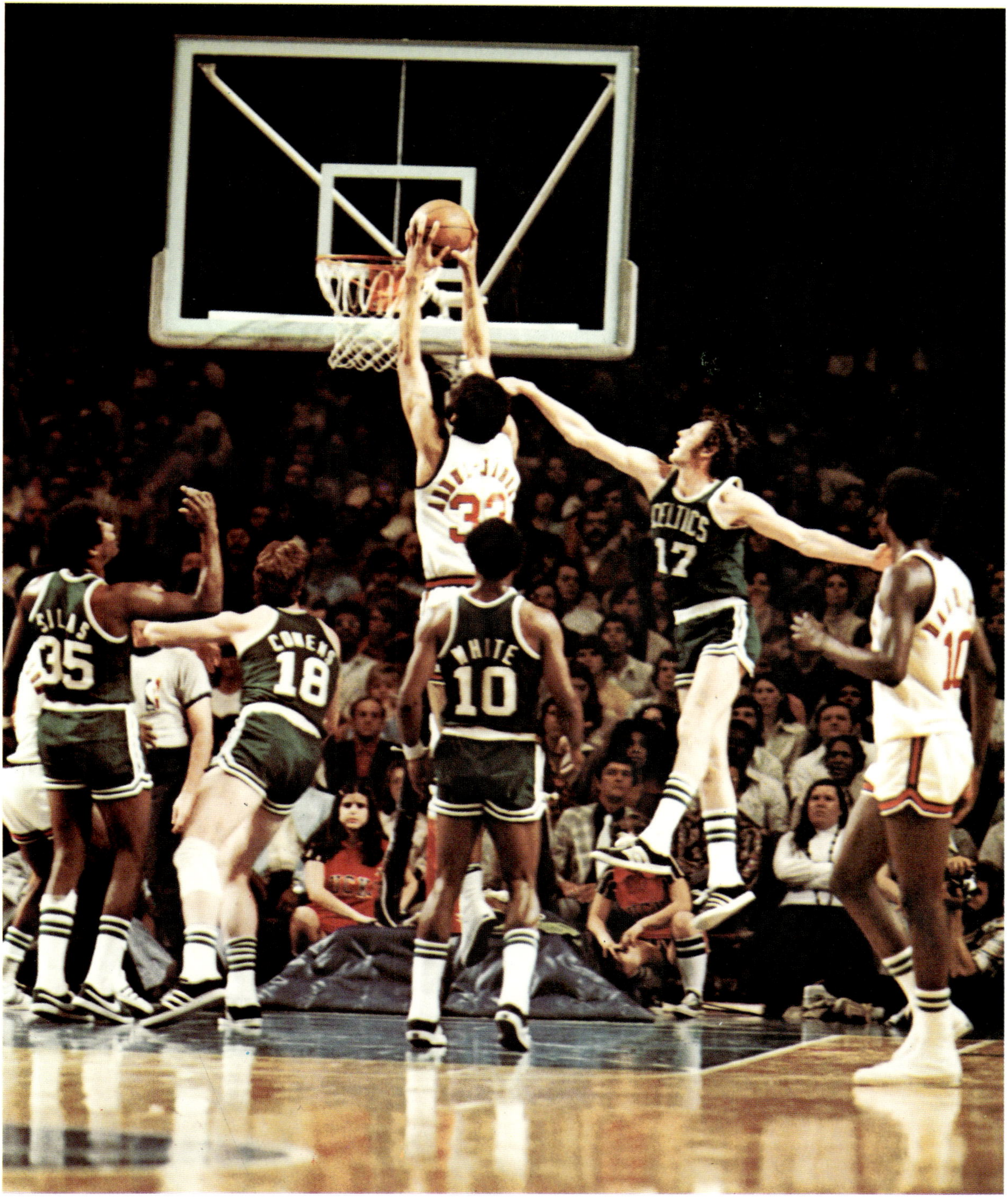
SILAS
35
COWENS
18
WHITE
10
CELTICS
17

small man with a crew cut. They talked for two hours. When they were finished, Arty decided to stick around. For a while, it was the right choice.

It wasn't long before Arty began to feel a little more comfortable, a little more at home. As the strangeness wore off, he started to look around, checking out the new world, a world far different from the one he had known.

He met people quickly. There were always some kids hanging around who liked to talk to athletes. So Arty found an avenue to get him past the awkward stage of meeting strangers. Before long, they were talking to him as a person, not just a basketball player. It was important.

He found himself studying them, learning what made them tick, learning where they came from. There were Polish kids from Pittsburgh; Jewish kids from New York; and all those husky, red-faced farm boys from the backwoods of the North. It was a collection he had never seen before.

There were also the brothers, the black kids, mostly athletes, who came from the same kind of place that Arty did. Their experiences were the same, and it was with the brothers that Arty felt most at ease. It was with the brothers that he'd go stepping out, doing the town, having fun.

Basketball was a different story. He played two years and packed it in. It was strictly a downhill trip.

Part of the reason was the atmosphere. In major colleges, the coaches and administration and alumni are very concerned with their image. The way sports are set up, the best way to keep everybody happy is to have a winning record. Nothing is as important as winning. Second best is nowhere. The old saying of playing the game for the sake of playing the game is just a line the coaches

47

haul out for the sportswriters when the team is in a losing streak. Underneath, they are burning. They can't stand the idea of losing; it makes them very unhappy. Sooner or later, if they lose often enough, they lose their job.

George Richland was worried about losing his job. He was tense and frustrated. He was nervous and unhappy. This is the way he came off to his players. This is what they remember about playing for him. There was no harmony on the team, no spirit. There was only a great gap between coach and players. The gap widened with every game.

The gap, of course, showed up most clearly on the playing floor. Arty's team didn't win very often. When they lost, they often lost big. It was a combination of coaching and limited talent.

George Richland may have known some basketball, but somewhere between his head and his instruction, what he knew was lost. His strategies were predictable. In a lot of games, the other teams had Richland so well scouted that they'd be moving to the spot on the floor where the play was supposed to be set up even before Arty and his teammates could get there to work the play.

To make matters worse, Richland had a way of making his men dislike him. He never got close to any of them. He was always "The Boss." The only times he'd give anyone special attention were the times when someone made a mistake. He was famous for yanking a player from the game right after an error. There are only so many times a proud kid can be humiliated before ten thousand fans. After that, he's angry and resentful. His playing suffers. Instead of letting his natural talents take care of themselves, he is afraid of goofing up. When you're playing tight, you don't play as well as you can.

Richland was also a disciplinarian. His own personal code was strict; he was a religious man, a nondrinker, a nonsmoker, a non-

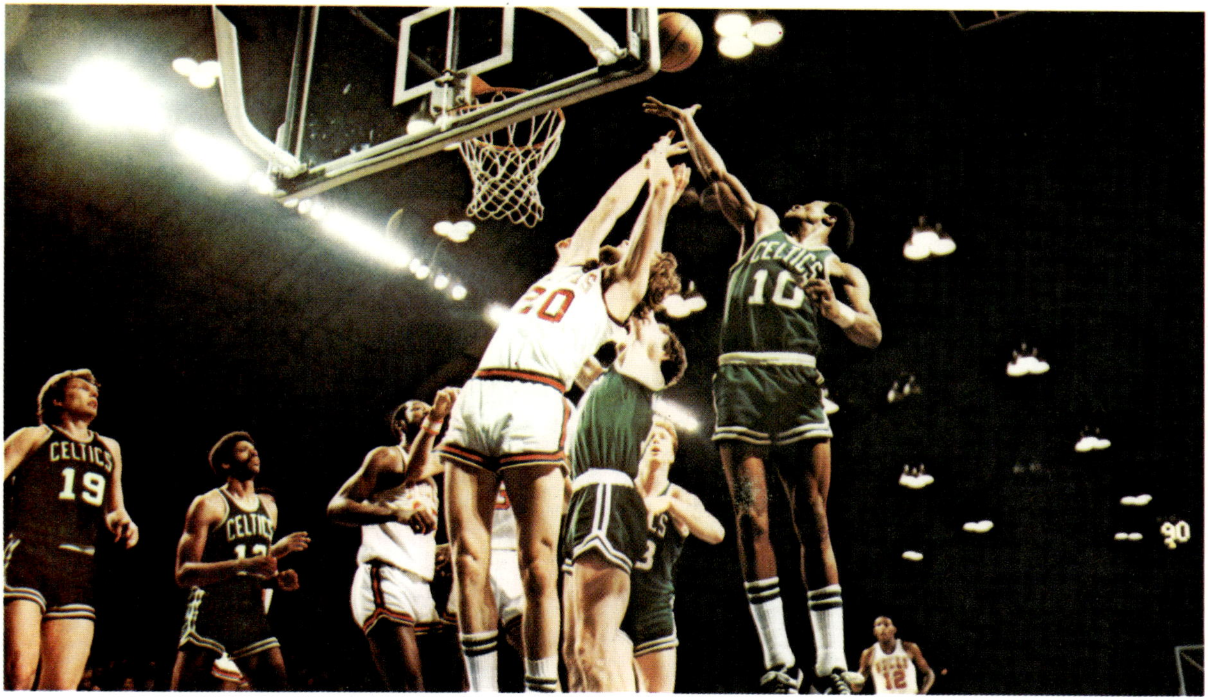
CELTICS
19
CELTICS
10
90

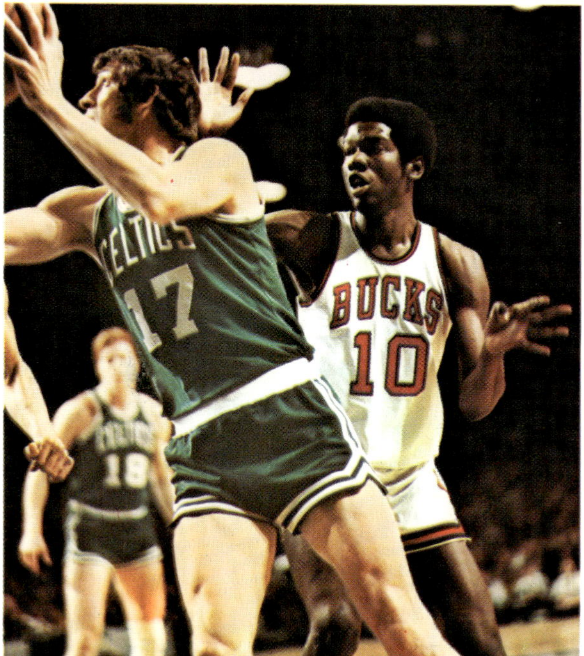
CELTICS
17
BUCKS
10
18

curser. He tried to pattern his team after himself. Anybody who didn't want to go along with him was soon in his doghouse. And once in the doghouse, there was no getting out.

For a while, Arty tried his best to keep out of trouble. He kept his mouth shut, went along with Richland's ways as well as he could, practiced, and played hard. He was a starting forward on the freshman team. The next year, he was riding the bench.

He's still not certain why, but he remembers one incident that probably had as much to do with his comedown as anything. It was during halftime of the Syracuse game. Syracuse was up by twenty-five points. In the locker room, Richland was mad. He delivered a ten-minute tongue-lashing, then threw a towel across the room in disgust.

"I've just about had it with you guys," he said. "I don't even want to coach you the second half. You're not worth the trouble."

He looked at each of the players silently and turned his back. "Jones," he said, "you might as well coach them."

Arty stood up and walked over to the blackboard. He picked up a piece of chalk and began to draw diagrams. Little Xs and Os.

"All right, you guys, here's what we're gonna do in the second half. We throw out the high post and we go to a double pivot to get more scoring out of Clark and Wallace. Take 'em to the boards, take 'em to the boards. On defense, we go to the press. Pressure 'em, pressure 'em. I want to see more of Ringling and Thomas in there, too. Jimmy, you go in for Coombs, and Larry, you start in place of Luksik."

Jim Ringling and Larry Thomas were in Richland's doghouse. They were two of the best players on the team, and everyone knew it. But they didn't follow Richland's code.

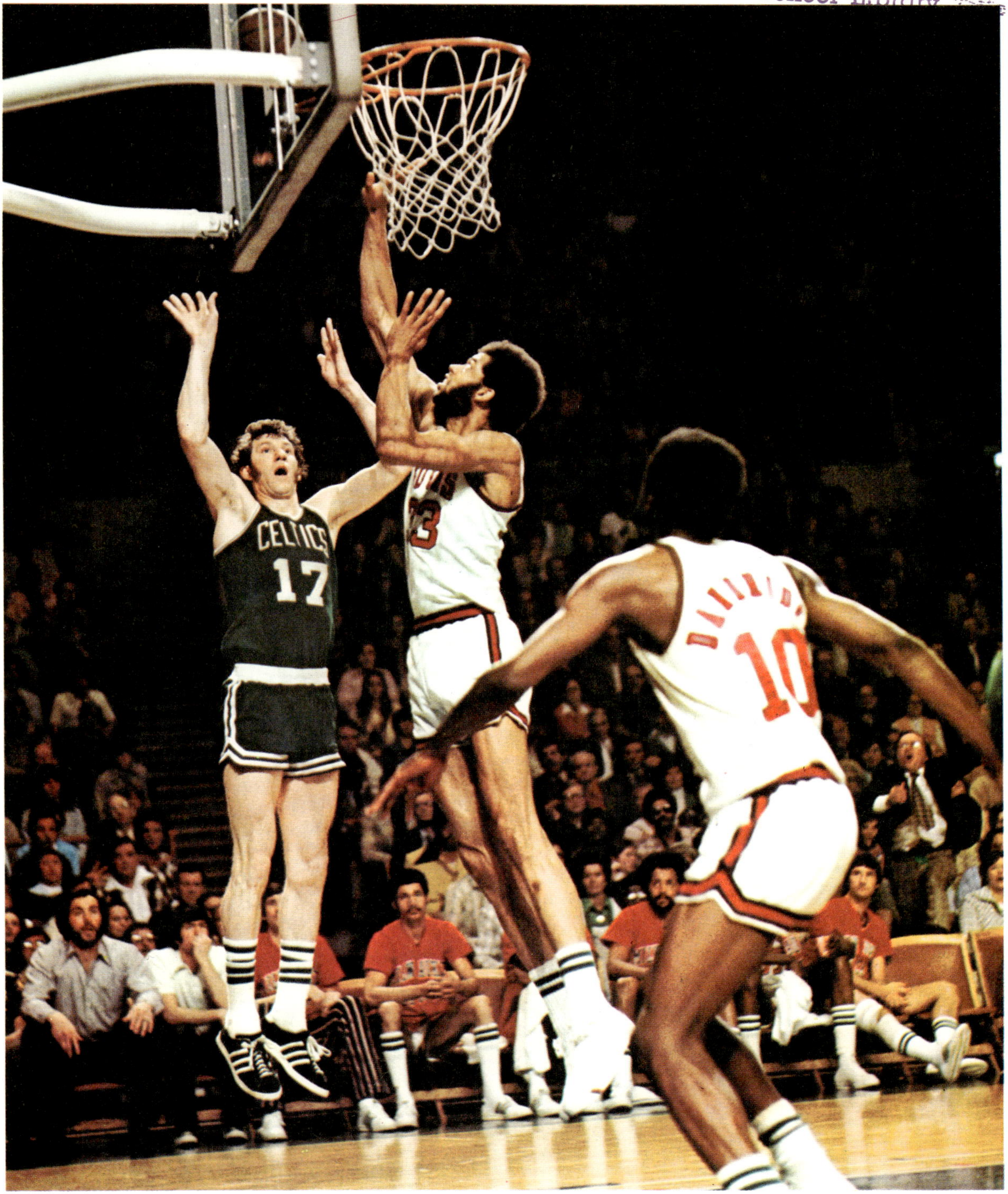
CELTICS
17
10

Richland was sizzling.

"Sit down, Jones," he said.

And that was that.

"Two years did it for me," says Arty. "I played a little bit more, spent most of my time with the scrubs. As far as I was concerned, none of it was worth it anymore. The ones who took it seriously were the guys who wanted to play in the pros. And on our team, we didn't have anybody like that."

"So what did you do?" asks Monte.

"Quit school. They told me the only way I could keep my scholarship was to keep playin' ball, and since I wasn't playin' ball, I didn't have any choice. I couldn't afford to pay my own way, and neither could my folks. I never went back after my sophomore year."

"Where did you go?"

"Joined the Navy and saw the world. Spent three years on a carrier. Got to puttin' out the ship's newspaper with some other dudes, and got interested in writing. I figured I knew enough about sports so that if I learned how to write someday I could be a sportswriter."

"You started with the paper after you got out?" asks Monte.

"Yeah. I got a job with the paper through a sportswriter I knew in college. I started out as a copy boy, got to writing obituaries, and one day they let me do a sports story. I wrote straight sports for three years. One day they came along and asked me if I'd like to try a column. So there you are. Here we are."

"Hey, from rags to riches, just like that," says Monte.

"Yeah, you could say that. But I don't see a whole lot of riches around here, do you?"

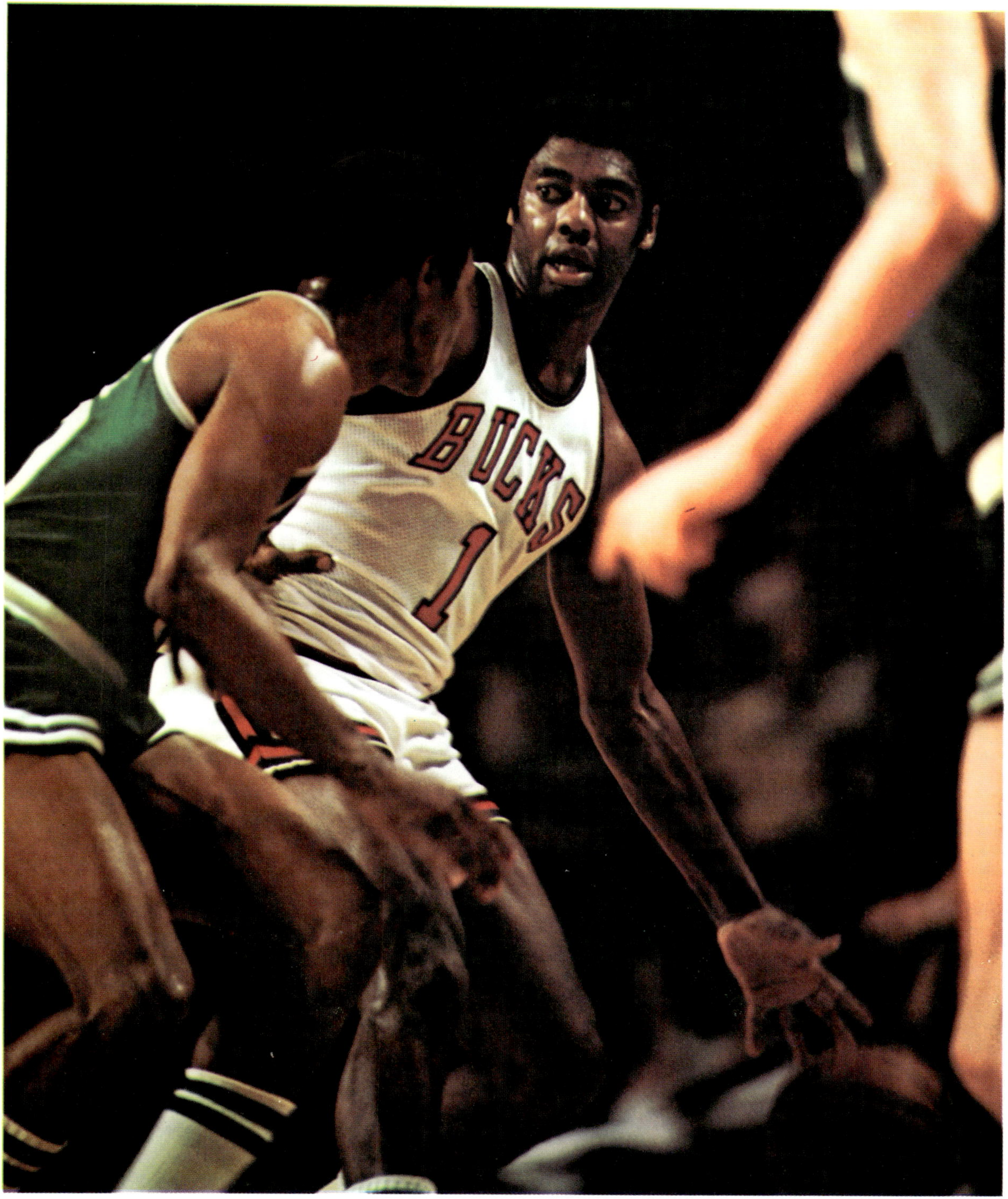
BUCKS
1

7
RALLY

The Bucks are coming to life! It is midway through the third period, and Kareem Abdul-Jabbar is starting to make a dent in the Boston defense. He is getting unexpected help from Mickey Davis. When they get around to talking contract next year, thinks Arty, Mickey Davis can say he was one of two men on the team who kept Boston from throwing the Bucks into Lake Michigan.

Arty looks down the press row. There must be a rally in the works — Ralph Petzer is yelling and pounding his fist on the table. One of these nights, thinks Arty, Ralph Petzer is going to have a stroke.

Kareem has found the range and Milwaukee's defense has tightened. If this keeps up, Arty is going to have to change the story he already has planned in his head.

Up to now, the Celtics seemed to have everything under control. Their defense has spoken for itself — Chaney harassing Oscar, Havlicek clamping down on Dandridge, and Cowens playing head-to-head with Abdul-Jabbar. Like Red Auerbach once said, "Without Kareem, the Bucks would be sweeping the streets."

But it has been the Boston offense that has been the real surprise. In all the games to

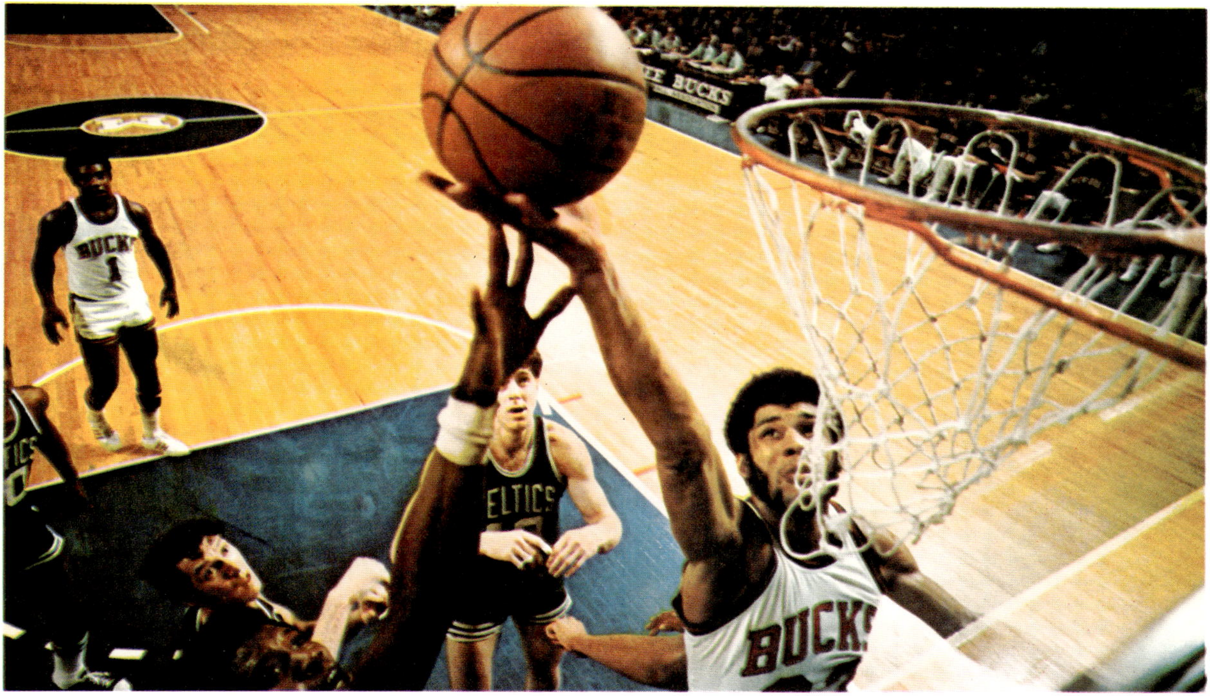

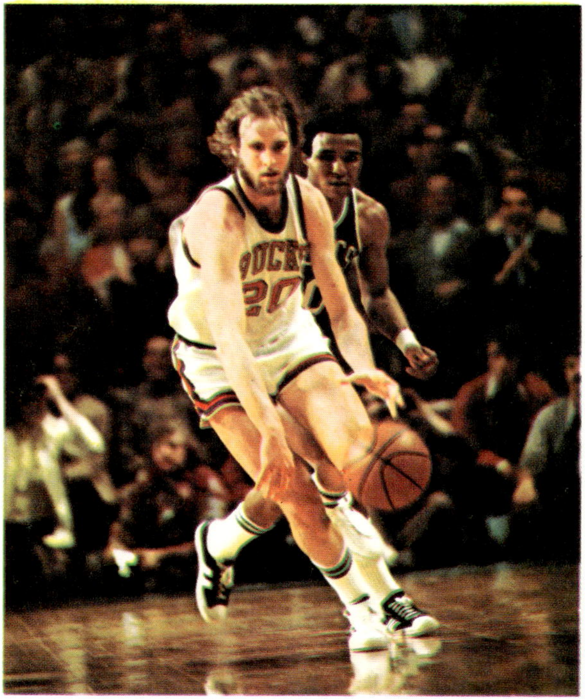

date, much of that offense has been John Havlicek. Havlicek has averaged twenty-eight points, many of them coming from the corner or on quick drives to the basket. Three nights ago, it was Havlicek's jumper with six seconds left in a double overtime that appeared to give the Celts the game and the championship. Abdul-Jabbar spoiled that with a picture skyhook at the buzzer.

Tonight, however, Havlicek hasn't been scoring as much. The Bucks have double-teamed him. Everytime he crosses into the offensive zone, there are two Bucks on his back like a blanket. But, Havlicek is serving a purpose. He has acted as the decoy, opening the offense for Cowens.

Cowens has been playing a high post, sometimes shooting arching jumpers, lofting them over the gigantic reach of Kareem, and sometimes passing off to his teammates, cutting for the basket. Beneath the boards, Cowens must grant Kareem an advantage in size. But by playing outside, where he has more room to move and use his quickness, he forces Kareem to follow. This leaves the lane open for the Celtics, and they have been scoring because of the open lane.

Now the scene has changed. It's 65-50 with seven minutes left in the third quarter. Cornell Warner has the ball and looks for Kareem. The big man scored fourteen points in the first quarter. In the next eighteen minutes he took only three shots and made none. Cowens has shut him off. But now Kareem slips away from the Boston center and takes Warner's pass underneath.

Thwunk! The Dunk!

In the next few minutes, the Celtics miss ten straight shots from the field and the Bucks score ten straight points. Davis gets four of them on jump shots and Milwaukee closes to 65-60. Jo Jo White hits two free throws for the Celts with little more than two minutes left in the quarter, but Jabbar counters

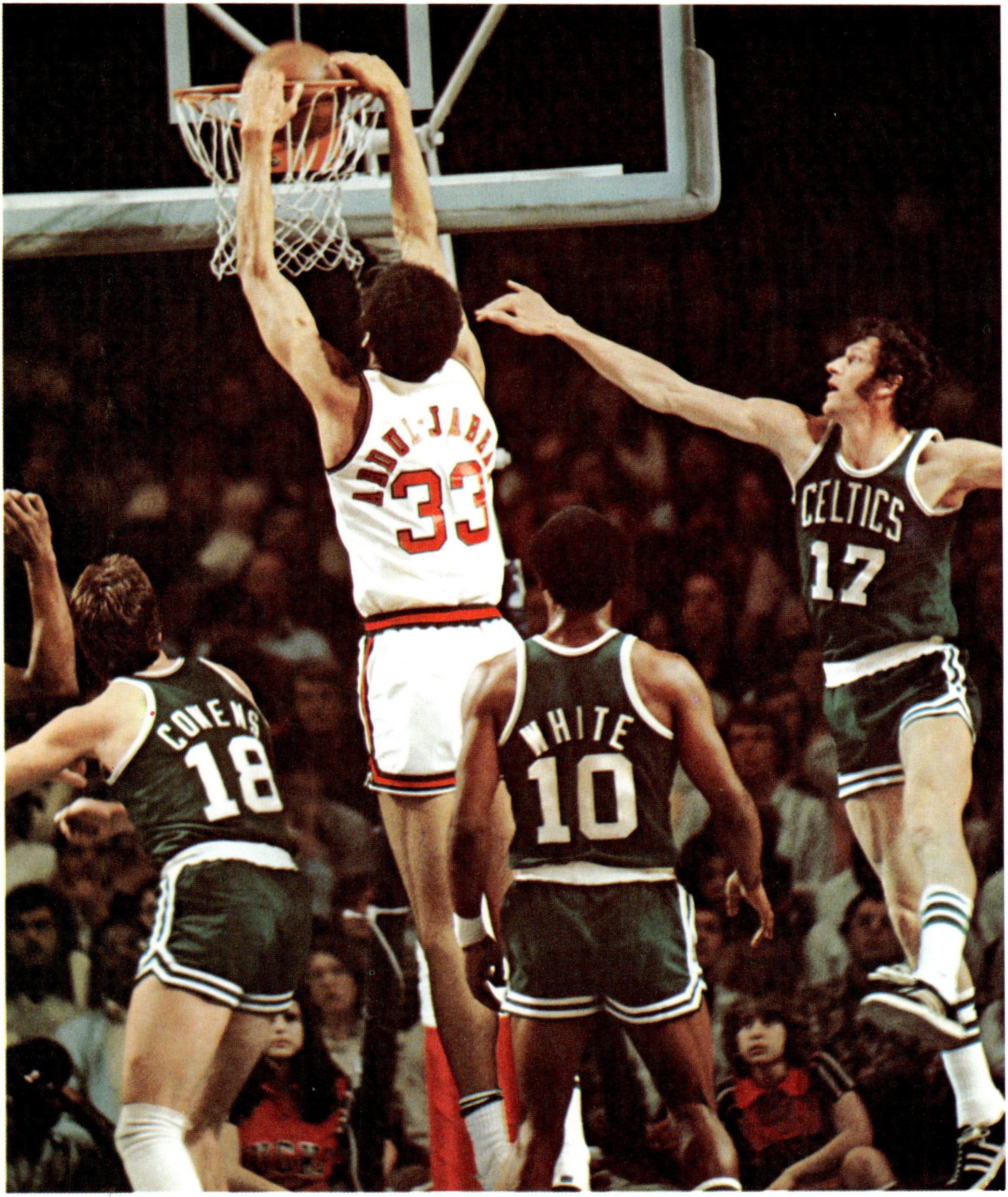
ABDUL-JABBAR
33
CELTICS
17
COWENS
18
WHITE
10

with a layup and Davis adds two more free throws on Paul Westphal's foul. The Bucks have closed to three.

Westphal drives the baseline to bring Boston its first basket in almost five minutes and the Celtics lead by five, 69-64. Jabbar cuts it to three again with a pair of free throws, but Havlicek comes back for Boston with a jumper from the baseline.

A whistle! It's Cowens fifth foul and the crowd goes wild.

Curtis Perry hits an eighteen-footer to cut Boston's lead again, 71-68.

Every fan in the Arena is screaming, stamping their feet. Ralph Petzer is red in the face and hoarse. Heinsohn is frowning fiercely.

But the rally has taken its toll. The Bucks are tired, their reserve strength is no match for Boston. The Celtics keep coming on, and Milwaukee is nearing its last gasp. Dandridge and Robertson foul, slowing the remaining momentum.

Cowens ignites another Boston surge with a sweet running hook shot. Inspired, the Celtics run off a string of eight points. Milwaukee refuses to give in, closing the gap again to seven. But that's as close as they're going to get. Boston pulls away again, sparked by the tireless Cowens. Arty Jones puts a sheet of paper into his typewriter, tapping away at his column.

"They were crying in their beer in Milwaukee last night," he begins, "and the tears they shed were for four stiffs and a superman who couldn't do it all."

Not real good, thinks Arty, but not real bad when you're fighting a deadline.

His column half finished, he strolls down to the locker rooms. There's really no one there he wants to talk to. There's seldom anything interesting said by a coach or a player immediately after an exhausting ball game. Besides, he doesn't like to share his informa-

59

tion with a couple dozen sweating sportswriters and TV newsmen. But it never hurts to pick up on the mood, even if it is usually predictable.

The locker room scenes are much like he thought they'd be. He stops off briefly in the Boston quarters to catch the Celtics celebration. The winners are tired, but obviously pleased. There are some shouts of victory, some weary laughter, and a little bit of soul handshaking. Tommy Heinsohn, the first coach to bring Boston a championship since Auerbach retired, has finally allowed himself to smile. He is telling the reporters that it was the greatest series ever. He is outlining the stategy that confused Milwaukee's defense — working down the middle, leaving Havlicek to draw attention at the baselines.

They are starting to break out the champagne when Arty leaves. He heads toward the morgue that will be the Bucks' dressing room. Losing locker rooms are one of the worst places anybody could want to be around. But it will be the Bucks' reactions that Arty's readers will want to see in the paper tomorrow afternoon. He probably won't quote them, just set a mood.

The mood is somber. Professional athletes take it very personally when they lose, especially when they lose a big one. It is a matter of pride, a matter of looking bad in front of the home crowd and a national television audience. It is a matter of being second best. You can talk all you want about giving your best effort and finishing second with honor. But to most professional athletes, there is no honor in being second best. There is only humiliation, anger, and disappointment.

A few of the Bucks are talking to the press, but they are only mouthing clichés. One player tells reporters the Bucks were "outhustled."

Arty spies Larry Costello, slumped on a

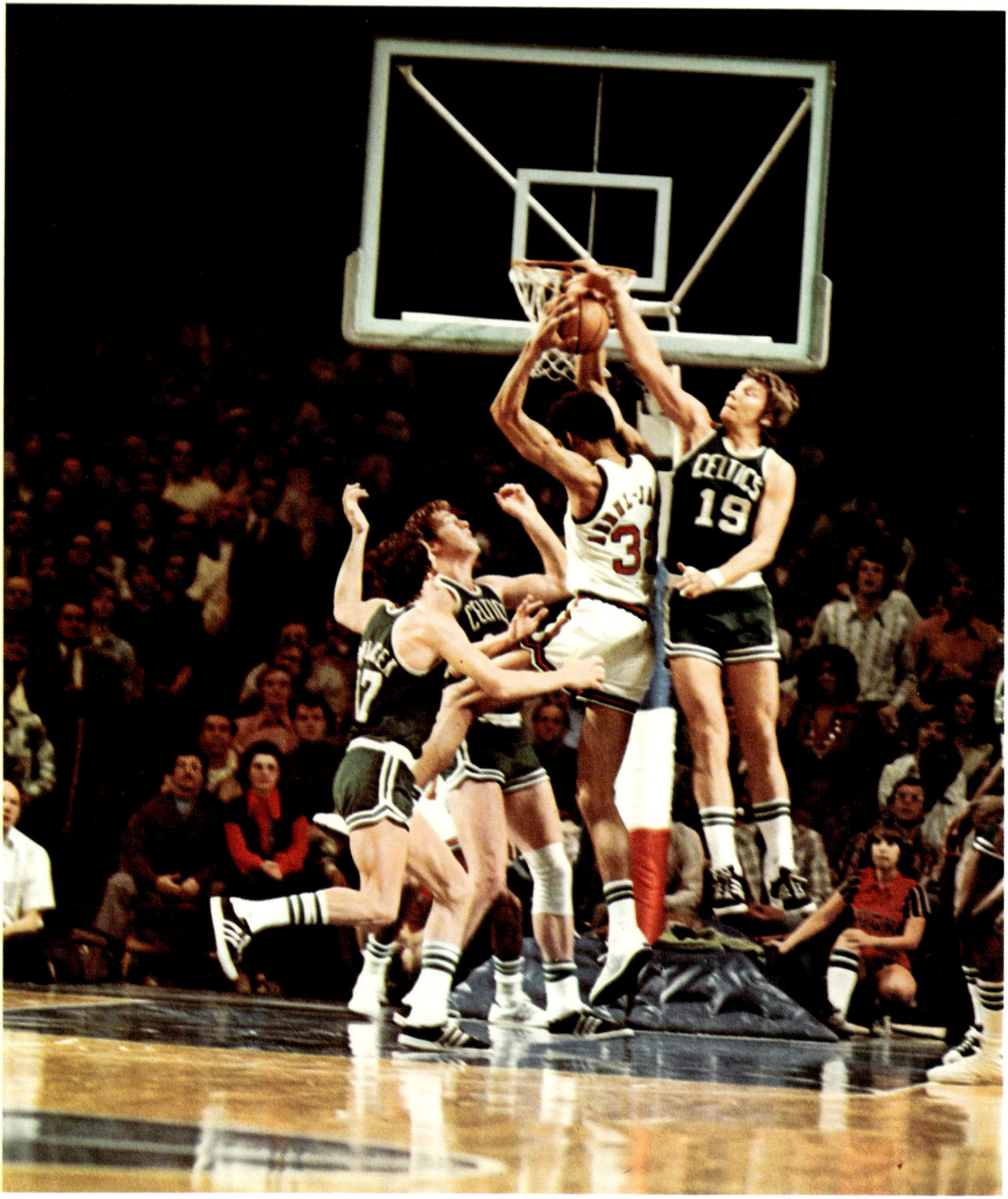
CELTICS
19
CELTICS

bench, his head down, his hands clasped between his legs, staring at the floor. He is giving short answers to the questioning of Ralph Petzer, who looks like he's going to cry.

Kareem is philosophical. He is telling reporters that he is a Moslem, that he accepts whatever happens, that all he can do is his best to make it come out the way he would like it to be. He tells them that victory and defeat are in the hands of the creator.

Class, thinks Arty, nothing but class. But do they understand? Do they really understand that Kareem is telling them a game is only a game, just another small part of something else?

Arty doubts that they do.

63

Pre-Reading Aids

1
It Beats Working

Purpose for Reading

Who is Artemus Jones?
How does he feel about what he does?

The answers to these questions are in Chapter 1.

Important Vocabulary

These words may be of help as you read:

column (col umn; kol′ əm), *n.*
a part of a newspaper written by a special writer

Sue writes a *column* for her school newspaper each week.

bulge (bulge; bulj′), *v.*
to swell outward

The weak spot in the tire caused it to *bulge* dangerously.

deadlines (dead lines; ded′ līnz), *n.*
time limits, the latest possible times to do certain things

If the *deadlines* for filing applications are not met, you will not be considered for a job.

complain (com plain; kəm plān′), *v.*
to find fault, to say that something is wrong

The job was done so poorly that he felt he had to *complain*.

porter (por ter; pôr′ tər), *n.*
a person who is hired to carry baggage

Mrs. Wheeler gave the *porter* a large tip because her bags were so heavy.

regulation (reg u la tion; reg yə lā′ shən), *adj.*
according to rules

Judy was not allowed to compete in the championship match because she had not been using a *regulation* ball.

65

Pre-Reading Aids

2
Thwunk! The Dunk!

Purpose for Reading

Why did dunking a basketball make Arty start thinking seriously about the game?

You'll discover the answer as you read this chapter.

Important Vocabulary

These words may prove helpful as you read Chapter 2:

regularly (reg u lar ly; reg′ yə lər lē), *adv.*
usually, as a habit

If you don't practice a musical instrument *regularly,* you are not likely to improve very much.

organized (or gan ized; or′ gən īzd), *adj.*
planned, carefully arranged

The party just seemed to begin; it had not really been an *organized* event.

fundamentals (fun da men tals; fun də men′ təlz), *n.*
basics, having to do with the basis or foundation

You must learn the *fundamentals* of a game well if you are ever going to become really good at it.

advantage (ad van tage); ad van′ tij), *n.*
something favorable or helpful

She had an *advantage* over her friends because she had played the game many times before.

comer (com er; kum′ ər), *n.*
someone with great promise or potential

He is young, but he has been so successful that he is thought of as a real *comer* in the field.

confidence (con fi dence; kon′ fə dəns), *n.*
firm belief in one's ability

The coach has great *confidence* about his team's chances of winning the game.

Pre-Reading Aids

3
More Than Just Fun

Purpose for Reading

What happened when Arty started taking basketball seriously?

What effect did Allen J. have on him?

You'll learn the answers as you read Chapter 3.

Important Vocabulary

You may find the following words helpful as you read this chapter:

semi-professional (sem i pro fes sion al; sem ē prə fesh′ ə nəl), *adj.*
played for money, but on a part-time basis

He was not quite good enough to play in the NBA, but he did play for a *semi-professional* team.

sensitive (sen si tive; sen′ sə tiv), *adj.*
having keen feeling, aware of others

I think people like Polly because she is so *sensitive* to their moods.

demanding (de mand ing; di man′ ding), *adj.*
requiring the best or greatest effort possible

Mr. Stanton is a very *demanding* boss; he expects hard work from everyone who works for him.

ability (a bil i ty; ə bil′ ə tē), *n.*
skill, power to perform

She has such great natural *ability* that she is almost certain to win the game.

alumnus (a lum nus; ə lum′ nəs), *n.*
a former student of a school

An invitation was sent inviting each *alumnus* to return for the homecoming game.

decision (de ci sion; di sizh′ ən), *n.*
choice, the settling of a question

Once the *decision* was made, it was clear to everyone what had to be done.

Pre-Reading Aids

4
Talent And Hard Work

Purpose for Reading

What is it like to play pro basketball?

You'll find the answer in this chapter.

Important Vocabulary

These words may be of help as you read Chapter 4:

climax (cli max; klī′maks), *n.*
the most exciting part

The *climax* of the fight came when he knocked his opponent down in the seventh round.

appreciation (ap pre ci a tion; ə prē shē ā′shən), *n.*
an understanding

Because he played the sport himself for so many years, he has a deep *appreciation* of how difficult it is to play it well.

especially (es pe cial ly; es pesh′ə lē), *adv.*
particularly

It is exciting to watch a good basketball game, *especially* if one of the players is your friend.

incredibly (in cred ib ly; in kred′ə blē), *adv.*
beyond belief, unbelievably

She is so *incredibly* good at the game that she makes everyone else look bad.

superb (su perb; su̇ pėrb′), *adj.*
excellent, very fine

Lou is a *superb* athlete—one of the very best.

reputations (rep u ta tions; rep yə tā′shənz), *n.*
what people think or say other people's characters are

They work as hard as they do because they want their *reputations* to be the very best.

Pre-Reading Aids

5
In A Jam

Purpose for Reading What makes a championship basketball team?

You'll learn in Chapter 5.

Important Vocabulary The following words may be of help as you read:

extend (ex tend; ek stend/), *v.*
to put out greater or the greatest possible effort

She will have to *extend* herself if she is going to have any chance of winning.

normally (nor mal ly; nôr/mə lē), *adv.*
usually, ordinarily

Jody would not *normally* have done that; this time was an exception.

combination (com bi na tion; kom bə nā/shən), *n.*
a pair or group of persons working together for some common purpose

The *combination* of Donna and Jim is a very difficult one to beat.

prime (prime; prīm), *n.*
best time, best condition, peak

He has never sung better—there is no question but that he is in his *prime.*

hampered (ham pered; ham/pərd), *v.*
held back, limited

Ben was *hampered* by an injury and could not play his usual outstanding game.

burden (bur den; bėr/dən), *n.*
heavy load, responsibility

As the others lost interest, the *burden* of waiting and worrying was left to him.

Pre-Reading Aids

6
A Whole Different Thing

Purpose for Reading

How did Arty react to the game?
Was college basketball what Arty expected it to be?

The answers to these questions are in Chapter 6.

Important Vocabulary

You may find these words helpful as you read:

objective (ob jec tive; əb jek′tiv), *adj.*
without bias, concerned about the way things really are

It is difficult to prepare an *objective* test in judging behavior.

atmosphere (at mos phere; at′mə sfir), *n.*
the feeling of a place

Peter was not sure why, but something about the *atmosphere* of that place frightened him.

image (im age; im′ij), *n.*
the impression a person makes (or wishes to make) on others

Dave acts that way because he wants to create the *image* of having a great deal of money.

harmony (har mo ny; här′mə nē), *n.*
agreement of feeling on ideas, getting along well

It takes a strong coach to create *harmony* on a team made up of many different playing styles and personalities.

strategies (strat e gies; strat′ə jēz), *n.*
plans

The *strategies* of the coach are so unusual that the players on the other teams are often confused.

disciplinarian (dis ci pli nar i an; dis ə plə nãr′ē ən), *n.*
a person who demands strict order and obedience of others

They did not listen to him because he was a good teacher, but because he was a strict *disciplinarian*.

Pre-Reading Aids

7
Rally

Purpose for Reading

How do the pros react to defeat and victory?
What does Arty think of Abdul-Jabbar?

Important Vocabulary

momentum (mo men tum; mo men/təm), *n.*
force or movement

Their drive toward the pennant seemed to gain *momentum* as they won victory after victory.

inspired (in spired; in spīrd/), *adj.*
aroused by, affected by

Inspired by the pep talk, the weary team returned to the field, determined to win.

morgue (morgue; môrg), *n.*
a place where unidentified bodies and the bodies of persons killed in accidents or murders are temporarily held

The bodies of the victims were taken to the *morgue* for identification.

somber (som ber; som/bər), *adj.*
gloomy, sad

Their faces were *somber* as they left the funeral.

humiliation (hu mil i a tion; hyü mil ē ā/shən), *n.*
a lowering of pride or dignity

The *humiliation* he felt when his crime was discovered was punishment enough.

clichés (cli chés; klē shāz/), *n.*
words or phrases that are so commonly used that they have little meaning

Many ads are so filled with *clichés* that they really don't say anything.

philosophical (phil o soph i cal; fil ə sof/ə kəl), *adj.*
thoughtful, accepting life and making the best of it

He was *philosophical* about what had happened because he could not change things anyway.

Discussion Questions

Chapter 1
What *one* word would you choose to summarize Artemus Jones' feeling about his job? (Be prepared to explain why you selected this word.)

Chapter 2
What event in your own life seems to you most like Arty's learning to dunk a basketball? Why?

Chapter 3
Who among the people you know seems most like Allen J.? In what ways?

If someone remarked that Arty had not earned the right to go to college, what would you say?

Chapter 4
Do you agree or disagree with the statement that pro basketball players are not worth their pay? Why?

Chapter 5
What were the two *most important* problems the Bucks faced in their championship game? (Be prepared to explain why you selected these.)

Chapter 6
If Arty had asked Petzer what he meant when he said, "Sometimes I think you're in the wrong business," what do you think Petzer might have said?

You're Arty Jones. You've been asked to explain why you quit basketball. What will you say?

Chapter 7
If Arty and Kareem were to talk about Petzer and about the championship game, what do you suppose they might say?

Related Activities

If basketball interests you and you want to learn more about the sport, you may wish to do one or more of the following:

1. Determine what resources about basketball are available in the school or public library. Prepare a list and a brief description of these. Make the list available to members of your class.

2. Invite a basketball player, coach, or official to speak to your class or school. Introduce your guest by mentioning the things you find most interesting. Write a follow-up letter thanking him or her for visiting.

3. Make a glossary of basketball terms that would be useful to someone who is unfamiliar with the game.

4. Make a photo essay of a basketball game.

5. Select words from newspaper and magazine articles, from radio and TV broadcasts, from the comments of fans and sportscasters, and from other sources of your own choice which capture the *feeling* of basketball. Use these words to make a collage or mobile or some other artistic presentation of basketball. (You may want to use the sound as well as the sight of these words.)

6. On a map of the United States, locate the home cities of the professional basketball teams. Label each location with the team name and the name of the arena where the games are played. Ask your librarian for help in locating this information.

7. Visit your school or public library and try to discover how and where the game of basketball began. Ask your librarian for assistance. If possible, use more than a single source. Summarize your findings and make them available to your class in oral or written form.

8. Draw and label a diagram of a basketball court, including its dimensions. Or, draw and label several diagrams to show how basketball courts have changed since the game began. You may want to ask your librarian for assistance in locating the necessary information.

9. Write to NBA or ABA headquarters. (The librarian can help you find the addresses.) Inquire about some or all of the following:

    official rules for NBA or ABA basketball
    statistics regarding players' salaries
    statistics on the length of professional careers
    statistics on the number and kind of player injuries
    responsibilities of the Commission
    other matters of interest to you

    Make your findings available to your classmates.

10. Create a basketball corner in your room. Try to capture the *feeling* of basketball—the action, the excitement, the strain. If possible, include both the sights and the sounds of the game.

11. Make a list of the NBA and ABA champions of the past several years. Include the names of the teams involved each year, the number of games played, the scores, and other information that seems worthwhile to you. Post the list in your classroom.

12. Teach one or more of your classmates, your teacher, or someone else how to read a basketball box score. Be sure to plan your lesson carefully. As a result of your efforts, your "audience" should be able to read a similar box score without help.

13. Visit the locker room of a winning or losing team after a basketball game. Try to capture the feeling you sense there. You may wish to use a tape recorder to record your impressions.

14. Prepare a brief biographical sketch of Kareem Abdul-Jabbar, Dave Cowens, or some other basketball player. Include pictures, if possible. Report your findings to your class in either oral or written form.

15. Make a tape recording of the sounds of basketball. Use the sounds alone—without adding words—to tell the story of a basketball game. Play the tape for your classmates. See if

they can tell you what has happened. (If they have difficulty, you may want to edit your tape and let them try once again.)

16. Attend one or more basketball practices. Try to decide how they are different from a basketball game. Explain the differences in oral or written form.

17. Conduct a poll of basketball players in your area. How many of them take the sport seriously? How does it feel to lose and to win? Make the results of your poll available to your class. Or, write up the results for use by your school or local newspaper.

18. Make a list of little-known facts about basketball. You might want to include some or all of the following:
the names and heights of the tallest players
the highest known game scores
the nicknames of well-known players
the size, date, and location of the largest crowd to attend a basketball game
other facts that interest you
Present your findings to your class in oral or written form.

19. Collect pictures from sports magazines and other sources that capture the feeling of basketball. Try to group these pictures by theme (for instance, the strain on players, or the coordination the game demands). Display the pictures in your classroom.

20. Invite a sports photographer to visit your class or school. Ask what a photographer looks for in covering a game and what problems are involved. Introduce your guest and be sure to write a follow-up letter of thanks.

Reading and Curriculum Editor	Peter Sanders, PhD. Wayne State University
Associate Reading Consultants	John Clark, M.A. Cincinnati Public Schools Cincinnati, Ohio Edward Daughtrey, M.S. Norfolk City Schools Norfolk, Virginia
Story Editor	Patrick Reardon
Associate Editor	Deborah Gardner
Coordinator of Learner Verification	Peter Sanders, PhD.
Related Activities and Vocabulary Sections	Peter Sanders, PhD.
Photography Editor	Eric Bartelt
Graphic Design	Interface Design Group, Inc.
Color Process	American Color Systems
Lithography	A. Hoen & Co.
Binding	Lake Book Bindery

Manufactured in the United States of America to Class A specifications of The Book Manufacturers' Institute

2 3 4 5 6 7 8 9 0   80 79 78 77 76